1977

EN D

day

THE CHEMISTRY OF THE RARE-EARTH ELEMENTS

TOPICS IN INORGANIC
AND GENERAL CHEMISTRY

A COLLECTION OF MONOGRAPHS EDITED BY

P. L. ROBINSON

*Emeritus Professor of Chemistry in the University of Durham and the
University of Newcastle-upon Tyne*

MONOGRAPH 4

Other titles in the collection:

1 The Chemistry of Beryllium *by* D. A. EVEREST

2 Inorganic Ion Exchangers *by* C. B. AMPHLETT

3 Introduction to the Atomic Nucleus *by* J. G. CUNINGHAME

In preparation

The Chemistry of Noble Gases *by* N. BARTLETT

Reactions in Liquid Ammonia *by* G. W. A. FOWLES and D. NICHOLLS

Metal Complexes and Ion-Pair Formation in Solution *by* G. H. NANCOLLAS

Carbons: Their Structure and Properties *by* H. HARKER AND H. MARSH

The Chemistry of Technetium and Rhenium *by* R. D. PEACOCK

The Chemistry of Niobium and Tantalum *by* F. FAIRBROTHER

The Chemistry of Selenium, Tellurium and Polonium *by* K. W. BAGNALL

The Chemistry of Titanium and Vanadium *by* R. J. H. CLARK

Fused Salts *by* G. J. HILLS AND D. KERRIDGE

The Chemistry of Gallium
by I. A. SHEKA, I. S. CHAUS AND T. T. MITYUREVA

Other titles to follow

THE CHEMISTRY OF THE
RARE-EARTH ELEMENTS

BY

N. E. TOPP, Ph. D., F.R.I.C.

Principal Scientific Officer,
National Chemical Laboratory, Teddington, Middlesex (Great Britain)

ELSEVIER PUBLISHING COMPANY

AMSTERDAM / LONDON / NEW YORK

1965

ELSEVIER PUBLISHING COMPANY
335 JAN VAN GALENSTRAAT, P.O. BOX 211, AMSTERDAM

AMERICAN ELSEVIER PUBLISHING COMPANY, INC.
52 VANDERBILT AVENUE, NEW YORK, N.Y. 10017

ELSEVIER PUBLISHING COMPANY LIMITED
RIPPLESIDE COMMERCIAL ESTATE
BARKING, ESSEX

LIBRARY OF CONGRESS CATALOG CARD NUMBER 65-12563

WITH 21 ILLUSTRATIONS AND 22 TABLES

PRINTED IN THE NETHERLANDS

The author of this monograph, Dr. N. E. Topp, died suddenly on 15th November 1964 at the age of 51 years. He had received the page proofs of his work, to the preparation of which he had brought much thought and enthusiasm, just before that date and had thus been deprived of the opportunity of making a final scrutiny of the text and preparing the index. Three of his colleagues immediately undertook these tasks and have completed them with scrupulous care and without delay. Although they wish to remain anonymous the thanks of the author's family, the publishers and the editor are due to them.

For a number of years the rare-earth elements had been Dr. Topp's major scientific preoccupation and perhaps this monograph is an appropriate memorial to a life too soon brought to a close.

P.L.R.

Preface

The rare earths are a fascinating group of elements, which have only recently become widely available in a state of high purity. The separation of these elements from one another was at one time regarded as one of the most difficult problems in classical inorganic chemistry. When the rare earth elements were identified as fission products from uranium, it became imperative to obtain more accurate physical data on the group, and this fact stimulated a large amount of work on modern separation techniques which was mainly carried out in the United States. An outcome of the success of this work has been the ready availability of the lanthanides for the first time, and as a result the past ten years has seen a notable increase in the knowledge of their chemical and physical properties.

I had spent several years working on various aspects of the separation problem when Dr. J. S. ANDERSON suggested that I should write a book on the chemistry of these elements. During my own work I had become aware of the need for an up-to-date reference book. In this book, I have endeavoured to review the known chemistry of these elements to the beginning of 1964. After a brief historical discussion of the discovery of the elements, their geochemistry and position in the periodic system are considered. Some typical methods of extracting the elements from minerals are described, and these are followed by a discussion of the more important separation techniques. In the following chapters, compounds of the lanthanides, and their properties, are discussed. The compounds fall into two categories, halides and salts with oxo-anions which are mostly soluble in water, and compounds such as oxides which are only known in the solid state. This is followed by a description of the analytical methods of lanthanide chemistry. In conclusion, a chapter is devoted to a consideration of the methods used in preparing the lanthanide metals and of their more important physical properties, followed by descriptions of a number of applications of these elements.

It has been my good fortune to be able to discuss many points which arose during the preparation of the manuscript with colleagues at Teddington, both in the National Chemical Laboratory and the National Physical Laboratory. I would like in particular to thank Drs. M. H. FORD-SMITH and C. R. VEALE for their critical comments on various sections of the text. The preparation of the manuscript has also been greatly assisted by Professor P. L. ROBINSON, whose constructive criticism has been of the utmost value. I should also like to express my collective thanks to the authors of a number of publications, and to their publishers, for permission to reproduce diagrams; individual acknowledgement is made in the text.

Finally, I must thank my wife for her help in preparing the manuscript, and Mrs. J. TAYLOR for typing the final draft.

Teddington, July, 1964.   N. E. TOPP

Contents

Editor's Note.   V
Preface.   VII

Chapter 1. *Introduction*   1
Discovery of the rare earth elements or lanthanides   1
Distribution of the rare earth elements in nature.   5
Electronic structures of the rare earth elements   6
Magnetic properties   9
Ionic size.   11
References   13

Chapter 2. *Extraction of the rare earth elements from minerals*   14
The rare earth minerals   14
The isolation of lanthanides from minerals   19
References   25

Chapter 3. *Modern separation techniques*   26
Sulphate separation   26
Exploitation of charge change.   27
Ion-exchange chromatography   28
Solvent extraction   34
Amalgam extraction.   37
Ion-exchange membranes.   37
Conclusions   38
References   39

Chapter 4. *Salts of the rare earth elements*   42
Salts of terpositive lanthanides   42
Double salts   46
Salts with organic acids   47
Ceric compounds   47
Salts of bipositive lanthanides.   49
Organic compounds   50
References   51

Chapter 5. *Solution chemistry of the rare earth elements*   53
Electrical conductivity   53

Transport numbers   54
Activity coefficients   55
Miscellaneous properties   56
Hydrolysis of the tervalent ions   56
The nature of ceric solutions   56
Complex-ion formation   57
Reduction potentials   59
Conclusions   60
References   61

Chapter 6. *Unusual valency states of the lanthanide elements*   63
Low valency states   63
High valency states   67
Conclusions   69
References   69

Chapter 7. *Compounds with elements from groups I, III, IV, and V* . .   71
Hydrides and deuterides   71
Borides   74
Carbides   76
Silicides   78
Nitrides   80
Phosphides, arsenides, antimonides and bismuthides   81
References   82

Chapter 8. *Rare earth oxides*   85
Structure of the oxides   85
Non-stoicheiometric oxides   87
Lower oxides   91
Properties of the rare earth oxides   92
Compounds of rare earth oxides with other metal oxides   94
References   96

Chapter 9. *Sulphides, selenides and tellurides*   98
Rare earth sulphides   98
Structure of the rare earth sulphides   102
Rare earth selenides   106
The rare earth tellurides   109
References   111

Chapter 10. *Analytical methods*   114
Classical methods   114
Instrumental methods   117
Radioactive lanthanides   122
Conclusions   123
References   123

Chapter 11. *The rare earth metals*   125
  Electrolysis from fused salts baths   125
  Metallothermic reduction methods.   128
  Distillation of the rare earth metals   130
  Purification of the rare earth metals   132
  Properties of the rare earth metals   133
  Conclusions   140
  References   141

Chapter 12. *Applications of the rare earth metals*   143
  Established applications   144
  Potential applications of the rare earth elements   148
  References   152

Isotopes of rare earth elements produced by pile radiation   156
Subject Index   161

CHAPTER 1

Introduction

DISCOVERY OF THE RARE EARTH ELEMENTS OR LANTHANIDES

The rare earth elements are the largest naturally occurring group in the periodic system. Although in fact they are not at all rare, the close similarity of their chemical and physical properties made the occurrence of several of them together in individual minerals almost inevitable, and also accounted for the considerable difficulties in separating them from one another. Indeed for many years the separation of the rare earth elements was rightly considered to be one of the most difficult problems in inorganic chemistry It is not surprising that over one hundred years elapsed between the isolation and recognition of an element like the rare earths, yttrium in 1794, and the discovery of lutetium in 1907. In the interval, nearly one hundred alleged elements presumed to belong to this group were reported most of which were eventually eliminated entirely on chemical evidence. In 1913 MOSELEY showed there were fourteen atomic numbers between lanthanum and hafnium, and this set an upper limit to the discoverable rare earth elements. Of these, all were identified and prepared to a certain degree of purity by 1907 except promethium (atomic number 61). This element was not isolated until 1948 when MARINSKY and CORYELL, using the new technique of ion-exchange chromatography, obtained it from uranium fission products.[1] The element is radioactive and an inactive isotope of promethium is unknown.

The atomic weights and isotopes of the rare earth elements are summarised in Table 1.[2] Although they are not rare earth elements, scandium and yttrium are included since they are precursors of the rare earth family in Group III of the Periodic Table. Both

TABLE 1

Element	Symbol	Atomic Number	Atomic Weight	Isotopes
Scandium	Sc	21	44.956	45
Yttrium	Y	39	88.905	89
Lanthanum	La	57	138.91	138, 139
Cerium	Ce	58	140.12	136, 138, 140, 142
Praseodymium	Pr	59	140.907	141
Neodymium	Nd	60	144.24	142, 143, 144, 145, 146, 148, 150
Promethium	Pm	61		—
Samarium	Sm	62	150.35	144, 147, 148, 149, 150, 152, 154
Europium	Eu	63	151.96	151, 153
Gadolinium	Gd	64	157.25	152, 154, 155, 156, 157, 158, 160
Terbium	Tb	65	158.924	159
Dysprosium	Dy	66	162.50	156, 158, 160, 161, 162, 163, 164
Holmium	Ho	67	164.930	165
Erbium	Er	68	167.26	162, 164, 166, 167, 168, 170
Thulium	Tm	69	168.934	169
Ytterbium	Yb	70	173.04	168, 170, 171, 172, 173, 174, 176
Lutetium	Lu	71	174.97	175, 176

elements are found in rare earth minerals, although scandium is rarely present in more than marginal quantity.

The terms "light", "heavy", and "middle" earths will be frequently used in this book. Although the terms are imprecise they are very convenient; by light earths is meant the elements from lanthanum to europium; similarly the heavy earths comprise gadolinium to lutetium; and the middle earths samarium to holmium. Yttrium is always present in the more important rare earth minerals, and is often a major constituent if the mineral contains the middle or heavy earth groups (p. 16). As many of its chemical properties are similar to those of the heavy earth elements, its chemistry will be discussed. Scandium, however, differs from yttrium and the lanthanides in some respects and its chemistry will not be considered.

Turning back to the discovery of yttria, GADOLIN isolated this element from gadolinite in 1794, a mineral now known to contain predominantly yttrium and the middle and heavy earths. Soon after this, in 1804, BERZELIUS and HISINGER examined cerite expecting to isolate yttria from the mixed silicate. Instead they found a new oxide and named it ceria. Cerite in its turn is now known to be made up of mainly the light earths. Both GADOLIN's "yttria" and BERZELIUS' "ceria" were later shown to be complex mixtures of oxides, and these two mixtures each provided a starting material from which the light and heavy earth groups were subsequently isolated.

MOSANDER pyrolysed the crude material termed "ceria nitrate", and extracted from the ignited residue with dilute nitric acid a new earth, lanthana (1839). Two years later (1841) he isolated a second earth, didymia, from lanthana itself. He then turned to Gadolin's yttria, and found it to be even more complex. By fractional precipitation with ammonia, he succeeded in obtaining three earths; yttria, terbia, and erbia (1843).

Nearly forty years later, DE MARIGNAC extracted a new earth, ytterbia, from MOSANDER's erbium nitrate (1878). It was from this ytterbia that NILSON isolated the oxide of the first member of

TABLE 2

Element	Symbol	Atomic Number	Descriptive Classification
Lanthanum	La	57	
Cerium	Ce	58	
Praseodymium	Pr	59	
Neodymium	Nd	60	LIGHT EARTHS
Promethium	Pm	61	
Samarium	Sm	62	
Europium	Eu	63	
Gadolinium	Gd	64	MIDDLE EARTHS
Terbium	Tb	65	
Dysprosium	Dy	66	
Holmium	Ho	67	
Erbium	Er	68	HEAVY EARTHS
Thulium	Tm	69	
Ytterbium	Yb	70	
Lutetium	Lu	71	

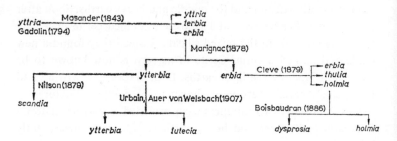

Fig. 1. Discovery of the heavy earth elements: separation of the heavy earths from yttria. [Reproduced, with permission, from *Research*, 11 (1958) 376.]

Group IIIA, scandia, which excited considerable interest at the time since its properties proved to be those required by MENDELEEV's predicted "ekaboron" (1879). Two further constituents of "erbia", thulia and holmia, were separated by CLEVE (1879), and soon after DE BOISBAUDRAN produced a third constituent, dysprosia (1886). More than twenty years later, URBAIN and VON WELSBACH independently obtained lutetia from ytterbia (1907). DE MARIGNAC also believed that Mosander's didymia was complex, and DE BOISBAUDRAN proved this was so by separating from it samaria in 1879 and gadolinia in 1886. VON WELSBACH isolated neodymium and praseodymium from didymium, by fractional crystallisation

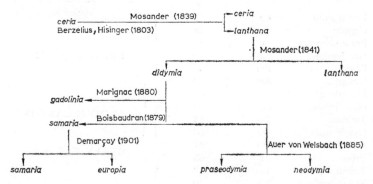

Fig. 2. Discovery of the light earth elements: separation of the light earths from ceria. [Reproduced, with permission, from *Research,* 11 (1958) 376.]

of the double ammonium nitrates. Finally, a similar procedure applied to the "samarium" magnesium nitrates led to the discovery of europium by DEMARCAY (1901). From 1850 onwards, the development of spectroscopic techniques greatly assisted identification of the various species. VON WELSBACH, who had worked with BUNSEN, made important contributions to the spectroscopy of the lanthanide elements.

In the early days, the accommodation of the rare earth elements in the Periodic Table proved to be a completely insoluble problem. There was uncertainty about their number and a Periodic Table based on groups and sub-groups which owed their existence to physical and chemical properties provided obvious places for only one such element, that now occupied by lanthanum. However, MOSELEY's atomic numbers solved this and other problems of the classification of the elements. In retrospect, the earlier work on separating the rare earth elements seems truly heroic, particularly when the limitations of the techniques and effort available are realised. It is, perhaps, fitting that the last of these elements, promethium, was isolated by a new means that has now supplanted the older methods of separation.

DISTRIBUTION OF THE RARE EARTH ELEMENTS IN NATURE

GOLDSCHMIDT's data on the abundance of the lanthanide elements in igneous rocks are summarised in Table 3, columns 1-3. For comparison, columns 4-6 show figures for the abundance of a number of other better known elements, not all of which would be considered rare.[3] It should be borne in mind that there is a tendency for elements to become less abundant with increase in atomic number.[4] Also, the abundances of the lanthanides given in Table 3 are all minute compared with the abundance of aluminium, which is 8.8×10^4 g/tonne.

Clearly, yttrium and cerium are by no means rare, being about as abundant as zinc and cobalt. Next come neodymium and lanthanum which run somewhat above the level of lead. The occur-

TABLE 3

COMPARISON OF ABUNDANCE OF LANTHANIDES AND OTHER
ELEMENTS IN IGNEOUS ROCKS

Element	Atomic number	Abundance, g/tonne	Element	Atomic number	Abundance, g/tonne
Y	39	31	Be	4	6
La	57	19	Co	27	40
Ce	58	44	Ni	28	100
Pr	59	5.6	Cu	29	100
Nd	60	24	Zn	30	40
Pm	61	—	Ga	31	15
Sm	62	6.5	As	33	5
Eu	63	1	Nb	41	15
Gd	64	6.3	Mo	42	15
Tb	65	1	Ag	47	0.1
Dy	66	4.3	Cd	48	0.5
Ho	67	1.2	Pt	78	0.005
Er	68	2.4	Au	79	0.005
Tm	69	0.3	Hg	80	0.5
Yb	70	2.6	Pb	82	16
Lu	71	0.7	Bi	83	0.2

rence of many other lanthanides is greater than that of beryllium and arsenic, and even europium exceeds silver and bismuth in abundance. Clearly, the lanthanide elements as a whole never qualified as rare elements and this has become increasingly clear as the methods for bringing them into a pure state have been so notably improved.

ELECTRONIC STRUCTURES OF THE RARE EARTH ELEMENTS

Of the lanthanide elements, lanthanum has a natural place in Group III A of the Periodic Table. Above it are scandium and yttrium, and below it is the element actinium. The four elements have many chemical similarities and are respectively the first members of the four series of transition elements, these being made up of elements with unfilled lower orbitals. In the first two transition series there are unfilled d-orbitals and in the last two which comprise the lanthanides and the actinides respectively there are unfilled f-orbitals.

The determination of the electronic configuration of a lanthanide or an actinide element is very difficult. The classical method depends upon a term analysis of the emission spectrum of the element.[5] The spectra of the lanthanides are exceedingly complex, and such an analysis has so far been made for only eight of these elements.[6-9] Results deduced from spectroscopy have been confirmed and supplemented by deductions from atomic beam resonance.[10-12] This method depends upon direct measurement of the electronic angular momentum, and the atomic g-values of

TABLE 4

ELECTRONIC CONFIGURATION OF THE LANTHANIDE ELEMENTS

	Atomic Number	1s	2s	2p	3s	3p	3d	4s	4p	4d	4f	5s	5p	5d	6s
Sc	21	2	2	6	2	6	1	2							
Y	39	2	2	6	2	6	10	2	6	1		2			
La	57	2	2	6	2	6	10	2	6	10		2	6	1	2
Ce*	58	2	2	6	2	6	10	2	6	10	1	2	6	1	2
Pr	59	2	2	6	2	6	10	2	6	10	3	2	6		2
Nd	60	2	2	6	2	6	10	2	6	10	4	2	6		2
Pm	61	2	2	6	2	6	10	2	6	10	5	2	6		2
Sm	62	2	2	6	2	6	10	2	6	10	6	2	6		2
Eu	63	2	2	6	2	6	10	2	6	10	7	2	6		2
Gd	64	2	2	6	2	6	10	2	6	10	7	2	6	1	2
Tb*	65	2	2	6	2	6	10	2	6	10	9	2	6		2
Dy	66	2	2	6	2	6	10	2	6	10	10	2	6		2
Ho	67	2	2	6	2	6	10	2	6	10	11	2	6		2
Er	68	2	2	6	2	6	10	2	6	10	12	2	6		2
Tm	69	2	2	6	2	6	10	2	6	10	13	2	6		2
Yb	70	2	2	6	2	6	10	2	6	10	14	2	6		2
Lu	71	2	2	6	2	6	10	2	6	10	14	2	6	1	2

* The configurations of cerium and terbium are still uncertain.

the atoms, from which the ground states can be deduced. Present views on the electronic structures are given in Table 4.

The nuclear charge increases in proton units, and with this increase successive electrons are added to the least energetic of the available orbitals. Considering first the Group IIIA elements scandium and yttrium, these have respectively the argon core with $(3d^14s^2)$ outer electrons and the krypton core with $(4d^15s^2)$ outer electrons. In their usual charge state of $+3$, the ions have the Ar and Kr configurations. After scandium, ten electrons are added to the 3d shell, and similarly after yttrium ten electrons are added to the 4d shell to give the first and second series of transition elements. However, in the third long period, the 5s- and 5p-orbitals have already been filled at xenon $(Z=54)$. Commencing with cerium, 14 electrons are added successively to the 4f shell to give the sequence of lanthanide elements; a similar addition of 5f electrons commences after actinium. The peculiarities of the lanthanide elements derive very largely from the deep-lying 4f electrons. Unlike the 3d and 4d electrons of the first and second transition series which project to the periphery of the atoms and thereby determine the possible valency states, the 4f electrons are shielded by eight electrons, $5s^2$ and $5p^6$, so that their chemical significance is so slight as to allow the remarkable similarity of the lanthanides.

The 4f electrons are not always added singly from cerium to lutetium although there is a tendency for the electron to enter the 4f shell rather than the 5d shell. The configurations of cerium and terbium are uncertain, but it is established that the 4f shell is half-filled at europium and filled at ytterbium. The normal charge state of the lanthanide elements is three, and the terpositive ions are formed by losing the $6s^2$ and generally a 4f electron, but sometimes the $5d^1$ electron. Thus the terpositive ion has the xenon core with 4f electrons. It is significant that no charge state other than three is known for lanthanum, gadolinium and lutetium. Some of the lanthanide elements have charge states of two or four, the ionic configurations being $(Xe) 4f^{n+1}$ and $(Xe) 4f^{n-1}$ respectively (p. 69). However, recent work has demonstrated that these higher and lower charge states are not confined to the elements immediately adjacent to lanthanum, gadolinium, and lutetium. It has been long argued that the unusual valency states are associated with the extra stability of the empty, the half-filled, and the filled 4f configurations, but it is now known that these oxidation states are more widely distributed and cannot be accounted for by this explanation alone.

MAGNETIC PROPERTIES

In common with many of the transition elements, most of the lanthanide metals and their compounds are strongly paramagnetic,* that is, they tend to align themselves parallel to a magnetic field. Paramagnetism is always associated with the presence of unpaired electrons, which make spin and orbital contributions to the magnetic moment. In the first and second transition series, the unpaired electrons lie in the 3d or 4d electron shells, but in the lanthanide elements they are in the 4f shell. It has already been stated that the 4f electrons do not take part in chemical bonding, since they are

---

* Paramagnetic substances are more permeable to a magnetic field than a vacuum, and the converse is true of diamagnetic substances. These properties are determined by measuring the force exerted on test samples by magnetic fields of known intensity. Thus, if a specimen is placed in a magnetic field of strength H, the relation between the field strength and the magnetic induction is: $- B = H + 4 \pi I$ where I is the intensity of magnetization. The quantity $I/H = K$ is the volume susceptibility; the term χ_m is used to denote the molal susceptibility. A convenient unit for expressing magnetic moments is the Bohr magnetion, β,

$$\beta = \frac{eh}{4 \, mc} = 0.917 \times 10^{-20} \text{ erg/gauss}$$

where e is electronic charge, h Plancks' constant, m the mass of the electron and c the velocity of light.

The magnetic susceptibility of many paramagnetic substances varies inversely with temperature according to the Curie-Weiss law:

$$\chi_m = \frac{c}{T + \theta}$$

where χ_m is the molal susceptibility, c is a constant, T the temperature of measurement, and θ the Curie temperature.

References p. 13

effectively shielded by the overlying 5s and 5p electrons. For this reason, there is an important difference between the magnetic properties of the lanthanides and the first two series of transition elements. Since the 3d and 4d electrons of the latter elements can take part in chemical bonding, their magnetic moments lose the orbital contribution when complexing occurs. Such reactivity is not displayed by the lanthanide elements, the 4f configurations being virtually unaffected by environment. This fact is of considerable practical consequence, as it means that the measurement of the magnetic susceptibility of a lanthanide compound gives a very accurate assessment of its charge state.

The magnetic susceptibilities of the lanthanide elements have been calculated by VAN VLECK, who derived an expression of the following form for the molal susceptibility:

$$\chi_m = \frac{N\mu^2}{3RT} + N\alpha$$

where μ^2 is a function of the low frequency part of the magnetic moment, and α is a function of the high frequency part of the magnetic moment, and of the diamagnetic effect. Solution of the equation required a knowledge of the principal quantum numbers of the lanthanides, which VAN VLECK deduced from the Hund rules. It turned out that the $N\alpha$ term was important only in the case of promethium, europium, and samarium, because of the population of levels other than the ground state.[13, 14]

The magnetic moments derived by these calculations are in remarkably good agreement with the experimentally determined values (Table 5).

The experimental values obtained are independant of solvent, anion, or complexing ligand. The same values have been obtained on solid oxides, solid hydrated salts, and solutions, and VAN VLECK concluded that even in solids the ions are virtually free as far as the 4f electrons are concerned. [14] This behaviour is unique among the transition elements; even the actinide elements, in which electrons are added to a comparable inner 5f shell, do not behave in this way.

Another important test for electronic structure can be made by

TABLE 5

MAGNETIC MOMENTS OF TERPOSITIVE LANTHANIDES

Ion	μ, Bohr magnetons		
	Theory [14]	$Ln_2(SO)_3.8H_2O$ [15]	$Ln(C_5H_5)_3$ [16]
La	0	0	
Ce	2.54		2.46
Pr	3.62	3.47	3.59
Nd	3.68	3.52	3.62
Sm	1.65	1.58	1.54
Eu	3.40	3.54	
Gd	7.94	7.9	7.95
Tb	9.7	9.6	
Dy	10.6	10.3	10.0
Ho	10.6	10.4	
Er	9.8	9.4	9.44
Tm	7.6	7.0	
Yb	4.5	4.3	4.0
Lu	0	0	

examining lanthanides in other charge states (p. 63). Cerium has a well known quadripositive state and ceric compounds are diamagnetic and isoelectronic with lanthanum(III) compounds. Similarly Sm^{2+}, Eu^{2+}, and Yb^{2+} are isoelectronic with the terpositive Eu^{3+}, Gd^{3+}, and Lu^{3+} respectively. In nearly all cases, the moments of the terpositive lanthanides are sufficiently well separated for magnetic measurements to give an unequivocal assessment of charge state.

IONIC SIZE

There is a general tendency throughout the periodic system for the atomic volumes of elements to decrease as their atomic numbers increase. The lanthanides are no exception to this, and the atomic volumes of their ions in tervalent salts decrease with atomic number. Atomic radii for co-ordination numbers of 6, 8, and 12 are summarised in Table 6.[17-22]

TABLE 6

RADIUS OF TERPOSITIVE LANTHANIDE IONS

	C.N. 6 Radius Å	C.N. 8 Radius Å	C.N. 12 Radius Å
La	1.061		1.346
Ce	1.034		
Pr	1.013		1.330
Nd	0.995	1.18	1.320
Pm	0.979		
Sm	0.964	1.14	1.310
Eu	0.950	1.13	1.304
Gd	0.938	1.11	1.299
Tb	0.923	1.09	
Dy	0.908	1.07	
Ho	0.894	1.05	
Er	0.881	1.03	
Tm	0.869	1.02	
Yb	0.858	1.00	
Lu	0.848	0.99	
Y		1.05	1.281

It will be noted that the largest contraction occurs between lanthanum and cerium, and also that the contraction from lanthanum to gadolinium is greater than from gadolinium to lutetium. Similar decreases in radius are shown by lanthanide ions in charge states other than three, and also by the lanthanide metals themselves (p. 136).

This successive reduction in ionic radius, known as the lanthanide contraction, does not occur elsewhere in the periodic system, because at no other point are 14 electrons successively added to electronic shells, none of which plays a part in chemical bonding.* At each increase in nuclear charge, one electron is added to the 4f shell. Owing to the shape of the orbitals, the shielding of these electrons from one another is imperfect. Therefore the effective

---

* A similar addition of 5f electrons takes place in the actinide series, but the evidence suggests that some of these are probably involved in chemical bonding. Thus many actinides display a much greater number of charge states than do the lanthanide elements.

nuclear charge experienced by these electrons increases, causing a reduction in the size of the 4f shell.

One of the most striking effects of the lanthanide contraction is displayed in the behaviour of yttrium. This element, which has a much smaller nuclear charge ($Z=39$), has a radius similar to that of holmium ($Z=67$). This is the reason why yttrium appeared among the heavy earths in many of the older separations; these depend on fractional crystallisation and basicity separations, in which the ionic radius or charge-radius ratio are important. The striking similarity between some other elements not belonging to the rare earth group, such as that between zirconium–hafnium and niobium–tantalum, are also due to the small size of the ion of the second element of these pairs caused by the lanthanide contraction.

REFERENCES

1 J. A. MARINSKY, L. E. GLENDENIN and C. D. CORYELL, *J. Am. Chem. Soc.*, 69 (1947) 2769.
2 Report of the Commission on Atomic Weights (1961); *Pure Appl. Chem.*, 5 (1962) 255.
3 V. M. GOLDSCHMIDT, *J. Chem. Soc.*, (1937) 655.
4 V. M. GOLDSCHMIDT, *Geochemistry*, Oxford University Press, London, 1954
5 G. HERZBERG, *Atomic spectra and atomic structure*, Dover Publications, New York, 1946.
6 W. F. MEGGERS, *Science*, 105 (1947) 514.
7 *Atomic Energy Levels*, National Bureau of Standards, *Circ. No. 457, Suppl. 3*, 1958.
8 C. E. MOORE, *Appl. Opt.*, 2 (1963) 665.
9 G. H. DIEKE and H. M. CROSSWHITE, *Appl. Opt.*, 2 (1963) 675.
10 A. NIERENBERG, *Ann. Rev. Nucl. Sci.*, 7 (1957) 349.
11 A. Y. CABEZAS, I. LINDGREN and R. MARRUS, *Phys. Rev.*, 122 (1961) 1796.
12 K. F. SMITH and I. J. SPALDING, *Proc. Royal Soc.*, 265A (1961-2) 133.
13 J. H. VAN VLECK and A. FRANK, *Phys. Rev.*, 34 (1929) 1494; 1625.
14 J. H. VAN VLECK, *The Theory of Electric and Magnetic Susceptibilities*, Oxford University Press, London, 1932.
15 A. SUCKSMITH, *Phil. Mag.*, 14 (1932) 1115.
16 J. M. BIRMINGHAM and G. WILKINSON, *J. Am. Chem. Soc.*, 78 (1956) 42.
17 A. ZALKIN and D. H. TEMPLETON, *J. Am. Chem. Soc.*, 75 (1953) 2453.
18 D. H. TEMPLETON and C. H. DAUBEN, *J. Am. Chem. Soc.*, 75 (1953) 6069.
19 D. H. TEMPLETON and G. F. CARTER, *J. Phys. Chem.*, 58 (1954) 941.
20 D. H. TEMPLETON and C. H. DAUBEN, *J. Am. Chem. Soc.*, 76 (1954) 5237.
21 F. BERTAUT and F. FORRAT, *Compt. Rend.*, 244 (1957) 96.
22 S. GELLER, *Acta Cryst.*, 20 (1957) 248.

CHAPTER 2

Extraction of the rare earth elements from minerals

THE RARE EARTH MINERALS

The rare earth elements are widely distributed in nature, and over one hundred types of mineral have been found which contain them. The elements have closely similar chemical properties; their usual charge number is three, they are strongly electropositive, and they have little tendency to hydrolyse. This similarity in chemical properties tends to lead to a concentration of several lanthanides in one mineral, or in a group of minerals. As a result, all minerals having rare earths as a major constituent contain an array of these elements; no known mineral contains only one lanthanide as a major constituent.

GOLDSCHMIDT has divided the lanthanide minerals into three categories.[1,2] The first are minerals containing major quantities of the rare earths and these are all associated with crystallizations from magmatic mother liquors of a pegmatic character. Typical examples of this type of mineral are monazite, which contains mainly the light earths, and xenotime, which contains yttrium and the heavy earths. Other minerals in this category are exemplified by euxenite and gadolinite; in these, however, there is a more uniform distribution of lanthanides.

The second category includes minerals in which the lanthanide elements form a minor constituent but nevertheless are still in the terpositive state. The most common minerals arise through the partial substitution of terpositive lanthanides for large bipositive ions such as those of calcium, strontium, or lead. Many calcium minerals, for example apatite, contain minor quantities of lanthanides. Cases are also known where the lanthanide substitution varies between wide limits, the extremes being a lanthanide and a non-lanthanide mineral respectively. Examples of this are found in the fluorspar–yttrofluorite and epidote–orthite systems.

In the third category, small quantities of lanthanides now in the bipositive condition replace large uni- or bipositive ions; this replacement is usually confined to the two ions Eu^{2+} and Sm^{2+}. Well known examples of this are provided by the presence of small quantities of europium in some minerals of the strontianite, fluorite, and potash feldspars types. The quantity of lanthanide is so small that they are not important as sources of the lanthanide elements. Comprehensive lists of lanthanide minerals are available in standard geological texts.[3,4]

The following are the most important minerals:

Monazite. A thorium–rare-earth phosphate, $(Th,Ln)PO_4$. The crystal structure is monoclinic. The thorium content reckoned as ThO_2 usually runs from 4% to 12%, but some exceptional monazites contain up to 30% of thoria. Other monazites also carry a little uranium.

The mineral is found as an accessory in granitic rocks, and in pegmatites. It is resistant to weathering and of high specific gravity, and some of the commercially important deposits are the products of gravity concentration by stream or tidal action. The mineral is widely distributed, with important deposits in India, Brazil, Australia, South Africa, and U.S.A. Associated minerals are xenotime, zircon, cassiterite, columbite, ilmenite, and apatite.

Bastnaesite. A rare earth fluorocarbonate, $LnFCO_3$. The structure is hexagonal. The lanthanide content is from 70% to 80% Ln_2O_3.

The mineral occurs in pegmatites and in weathered granitic deposits, associated with cerite, fluorite, and allanite. It has been found in a number of areas in Europe and Africa, but the only commercially important deposit is in California, U.S.A.

Gadolinite. A mixed silicate of the lanthanides, iron, and beryllium, $(Be,Fe)Ln_2Si_2O_{10}$. The mineral is found in Scandinavia and U.S.A.

Xenotime. A rare earth phosphate, $LnPO_4$. The mineral is tetragonal. The lanthanide content is from 55% to 70% Ln_2O_3 and

TABLE 7

DISTRIBUTION OF ELEMENTS IN

Mineral	La_2O_3	CeO_2	Pr_6O_{11}	Nd_2O_3	Sm_2O_3	Gd_2O_3
Monazite	17.0	53.5	2.6	17	2.6	2
Xenotime		0.6	0.1	0.5	1.0	2
Euxenite	2.9	5.8	0.8	3.2	2.5	5

some xenotimes may contain up to 4% of uranium, and a little thorium.

The mineral is found in acidic, that is highly silicious igneous rocks and pegmatites. Deposits usually also contain monazite, zircon, rutile, anatase and, less frequently, fergusonite and other niobium–tantalum minerals. The mineral is widely distributed. Deposits in Malaya and Nigeria are associated with niobium–tantalum minerals.

Euxenite and polycrase form a series of minerals with the composition $(Ln,U,Th)(Nb,Ta,Ti)_2O_6$; euxenites are high in niobium–tantalum content, and the polycrase minerals are high in titanium. The lanthanides usually run from 20 to 30% Ln_2O_3 with uranium and thorium varying from 5-10% and 1-5% respectively. The niobium–tantalum content of a euxenite is from 25-50% Nb_2O_5 and Tb_2O_5, the ratio of the two elements varying from 3 : 1 to 1 : 3.

The compositions of the lanthanide fractions from three of these minerals, namely a monazite, an euxenite, and a xenotime, are given in Table 7. All the minerals fall into GOLDSCHMIDT's first category.

Lanthanide distributions are shown diagramatically in Figs. 3, 4 and 5. The first two minerals, monazite and xenotime, have a high lanthanide content, but although monazite contains mainly the light earth elements, the predominant element in xenotime is yttrium, together with smaller quantities of the heavy earths. It is characteristic of the xenotime types of mineral that yttrium is the largest single constitutent. These two types of mineral are typical of the selective assemblage, which must be due to limitations

THREE LANTHANIDE MINERALS

Tb_4O_7	Dy_2O_3	Ho_2O_3	Er_2O_3	Tm_2O_3	Yb_2O_3	Lu_2O_3	Y_2O_3
0.7	0.8	0.15			0.15	0.1	3
1	14.5	2.5	12.5	2	17	3	45
1.3	10.7	2	8	0.5	6	0.3	50

on cation size imposed by the structure of the mineral. The amount of rare earth material in minerals such as euxenite and gadolinite is relatively low, and the lanthanide distribution more uniform.

Three important conclusions can be drawn from these facts. *(1)* The abundance of the lanthanide elements varies markedly

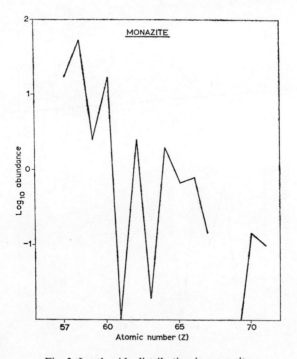

Fig. 3. Lanthanide distribution in monazite.

from one mineral to another. *(2)* Whether the mineral happens to be rich in the light or heavy earths, the whole assemblage of lanthanides is present even though some may be there in very minor amounts. *(3)* Superimposed on this pattern is one which arises from the general fact that elements of even atomic number are always considerably more abundant than those of odd atomic number. The even–odd variation in lanthanide abundance is probably the most clearly defined example of the Oddo and Harkins rule.[5, 6] This generalisation, which applies throughout the Periodic Table, is thought to arise from nucleii which have equal numbers of protons and neutrons being inherently more stable than those which have an unpaired proton or neutron.[7]

The element scandium, which is similar in some respects to the lanthanides, is found in some rare earth minerals but always

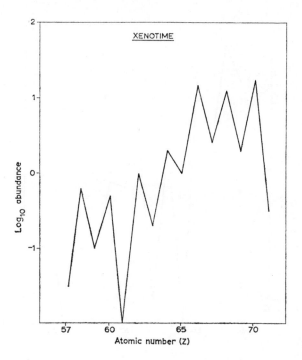

Fig. 4. Lanthanide distribution in xenotime.

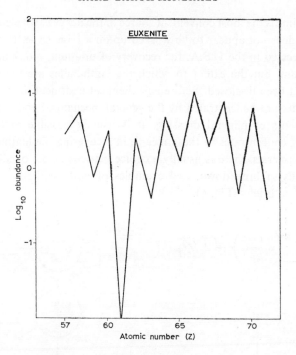

Fig. 5. Lanthanide distribution in euxenite.

in small proportions; only one known mineral, the very rare silicate thortveitite, $(LnSc)Si_2O_{10}$, contains large quantities of scandium.

ISOLATION OF THE LANTHANIDES FROM MINERALS

It will be clear from the previous discussion that the breakdown of the mineral and isolation of the lanthanide fraction is only the first step to be taken in the isolation of pure lanthanide material and that for elements of even atomic number, this task can be eased considerably by the selection of a suitable mineral.

The two minerals of current economic importance are monazite and bastnaesite, both of which are sources of the light earths.

Xenotime is the most convenient source of the heavy earth elements, but it does not appear to be worked up on a large scale. Euxenite is processed in the U.S.A. for recovery of uranium, niobium, and tantalum, but the extent to which the lanthanides are recovered has not been disclosed. Before any chemical treatment, lanthanide minerals are concentrated by the general mechanical and physical treatments of mineral dressing. It is usually possible to obtain > 90% concentrates by these means. In recovering the lanthanides from minerals, there is usually a choice between acidic or alkaline methods of breakdown, and examples of both methods will be described briefly (Fig. 6).

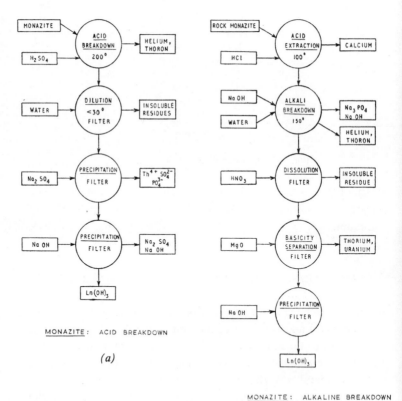

Fig. 6. Extraction of lanthanides from monazite: *(a)*, acid; *(b)*, alkaline.

Monazite. Acid breakdown. Monazite sands are suitable for acidic attack since the calcium content of the mineral is often low. Both lanthanide and thorium phosphates are very insoluble in water; the problem is to separate the lanthanides from the thorium, and to remove the phosphate anion.

The sand is slowly added to concentrated sulphuric acid at 200–220°, in the proportion one part of monazite to 2–3 of acid; the reaction is highly exothermic, and helium and thoron are released as the mineral dissolves (Fig. 6 *(a)*). Barium sulphate (1 lb per ton of monazite) is added as a collector for mesothorium. Reaction is complete in 2–3 h, and the product is allowed to cool.

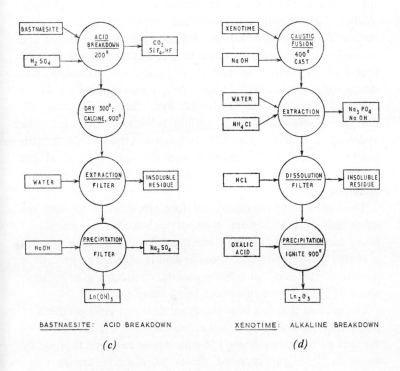

BASTNAESITE: ACID BREAKDOWN

(c)

XENOTIME: ALKALINE BREAKDOWN

(d)

Fig. 6. Extraction of lanthanides from *(c)* bastnaesite and *(d)* xenotime.

References p. 25

The pasty reaction product is cautiously diluted with water (ten times the weight of the mineral), with cooling to prevent the temperature from rising above 30°. The solution is filtered, the residue washed, and the washings combined with the filtrate.

$$(\text{Ln Th})PO_4 \xrightarrow{\text{H}_2\text{SO}_4} Ln_2(SO_4)_3 + Th(SO_4)_2 + H_3PO_4$$

The sulphate solution is moderately stable; it is approximately 3 N in sulphuric acid, and 1 N in phosphate, and contains about 50–60 g/l of Ln_2O_3, and 5–6 g/l of ThO_2, both as sulphates.

To the cold and stirred solution, sodium sulphate is added in the proportion 4 moles sodium sulphate per mole of lanthanide. Within thirty minutes, a crystalline precipitate of the sodium lanthanide double-sulphates is obtained. This if filtered off, and washed with 0.3 N sodium sulphate. The washings, containing the excess of sulphuric and phosphoric acids, are discarded. The double-sulphates are boiled with a 10% excess of caustic soda for thirty minutes, and the lanthanide hydroxides are filtered off; the filtrate, essentially 3 M sodium sulphate, is recycled. The hydroxide cake is dried at 120° to oxidise cerium to the quadripositive state. The dry material contains roughly half of the thorium, which has formed mixed crystals with the rare-earth double-sulphates.

The filtrate from the double-sulphate precipitation contains the other half of the thorium, together with a smaller amount of heavy earth double-sulphates, which are also present. The solution is heated to 90°, and 15g/l of oxalic acid is added. The product is a thorium–rare-earth phosphate oxalate, containing after ignition about 95% ThO_2, the remainder being heavy earths.[8, 9]

The process that has been described does not yield products of high purity, but the separation is rapid. There are a large number of variants on this process, and these have been reviewed thoroughly by WYLIE.[10] Highly purified grades of thorium are required for many nuclear applications. This requirement is met by subjecting the thorium to solvent extraction from acidic nitrate solutions, the extractant being tri-*n*-butyl phosphate (TBP). Any uranium present may also be separated and purified.[11]

Monazite. Alkaline breakdown. When rock monazites are used in this process (Fig. 6 *(b)*) it is necessary first to boil the mineral with nitric or hydrochloric acid (8N) to remove calcium, which is present as apatite. Any thorium extracted with the calcium is recovered by precipitation of the acid liquor at pH 1.8, and returned to the process. The mineral is then heated under reflux with 50% aqueous caustic soda, in the proportion 1.2 parts caustic soda per part monazite. Reaction is complete in two or three hours, and the mixed thorium–lanthanide hydroxides are filtered off while hot.

$$(\text{Ln, Th})\text{PO}_4 \xrightarrow{\text{NaOH}} \text{Ln(OH)}_3 + \text{Th(OH)}_4 + \text{Na}_3\text{PO}_4$$

The precipitate is carefully washed to remove phosphate. The filtrate is concentrated and the sodium phosphate which separates is filtered off. A part of the recovered alkali is recycled.

The hydrous oxides are dissolved in nitric acid, and filtered from unreacted monazite and insoluble material. Advantage is taken of the fact that thorium and uranium hydrolyse much more readily than the terpositive lanthanides to effect a basicity separation. A cleaner separation can be obtained if the pH is slowly increased to 5.6; for this reason magnesia or ammonia are stirred into the solution under controlled conditions. The thorium and uranium precipitates are filtered off, and purified by solvent extraction with TBP from nitrate solutions. The rare earths are precipitated as hydroxides and the filter cake is dried for the removal of cerium as the dioxide.[12]

An interesting variant on this process has recently been proposed by KRAITZER.[13] Instead of relying upon a basicity separation, the mixed thorium–lanthanide hydroxide is extracted with a sodium carbonate buffer at pH 9.5–10.0. The thorium enters the solution as a carbonate complex, and, after four extractions, a recovery of 99.8% of the thorium is claimed.

Bastnaesite; Acid breakdown. In the Californian deposit, the mineral is present to the extent of 10% in a complex ore body. Concentrates containing over 70% of the fluorocarbonate are obtained by normal mineral processing. The problem is to attack the lanthanide mineral selectively and render non-lanthanides insoluble in water.

The finely ground mineral is slowly added to concentrated sulphuric acid at 200°, in the proportion one part of bastnaesite to 1.3 parts of acid (Fig. 6 (c)). There is a vigorous exothermic reaction, carbon dioxide, hydrofluoric acid, and silcon tetrafluoride being evolved.

$$2\,LnFCO_3 + 3\,H_2SO_4 \rightarrow Ln_2(SO_4)_3 + 2\,CO_2 + 2\,HF + 2\,H_2O$$

The product is dried at 500°, and the temperature is raised to 900° to decompose the acid sulphates; this heating also renders the contaminants insoluble in water. The dry product is leached with cold water, and filtered, to give a solution of lanthanide sulphates containing approximately 50 g/l Ln_2O_3. From this solution, lanthanides are recovered by precipitation as hydroxides or oxalates.[14]
Xenotime. Alkaline breakdown. The mineral is a lanthanide phosphate, and concentrates containing 90% of xenotime may be obtained by physical separation.

The mineral is cautiously added to molten caustic soda at 400°, in the proportion one part of mineral to 1.75 parts of alkali (Fig. 6 (d)). The reaction is exothermic, and after one hour the product is cooled by pouring it as thin layers into mild steel trays.

$$LnPO_4 + 3NaOH \rightarrow Ln(OH)_3 + Na_3PO_4$$

After cooling, the solid is extracted with water to remove phosphate and the excess of alkali. To prevent excessive swelling of the hydroxide, the final washings are carried out with dilute salt solution. The hydroxides are dissolved in the minimum of hydrochloric acid and filtered from residual mineral and insoluble material (*e.g.* silica, cassiterite), and the lanthanides are recovered from the solution by precipitation as oxalates.[15]

REFERENCES

1 V. M. GOLDSCHMIDT and L. THOMASSEN, *Videnskaps Skrift 1*, Mat. naturw. Kl. (1924), No. 5.

2 V. M. GOLDSCHMIDT, *Geochemistry*, p. 306, Oxford University Press, Oxford, 1954.

3 W. A. DEER, R. A. HOWIE and J. ZUSSMAN, *Rock-Forming Minerals*, Longman's Green, London, 1962.

4 C. PALACHE, A. BERMAN and C. FRONDEL, *Dana's System of Minerology*, John Wiley, New York, 7th Ed., 1944.

5 G. ODDO, *Z. Anorg. Chem.*, 87 (1914) 253.

6 W. D. HARKINS, *J. Am. Chem. Soc.*, 39 (1917) 856.

7 K. RANKHAMA and T. G. SAHAMA, *Geochemistry*, Chapt. 2, Chicago University Press, 1950.

8 E. S. PILKINGTON and A. W. WYLIE, *J. Soc. Chem. Ind.*, 66 (1947) 387.

9 R. W. URIE, *J. Soc. Chem. Ind.*, 66 (1947) 437.

10 A. W. WYLIE, *Rev. Pure Appl. Chem.*, 9 (1959) 169.

11 A. AUDSLEY, R. LIND and P. C. ENGLAND, *Symposium on Extraction and Refining of Rare Metals*, p. 351, Inst. Mining Metallurgy, 1957.

12 A. E. BEARSE, G. D. CALKINS, J. W. CLEGG and R. W. FILBERT, *Chem. Eng. Progr.*, 50 (1954) 235.

13 I. C. KRAITZER, *Aust. Inst. Mining* and *Metallurgy*, 205 (1963) 69.

14 VAN E. SHAW, *U. S. Bur. Mines, Rept. Invest.*, 5474 (1959).

15 F. H. HOWIE and N. E. TOPP, unpublished work.

CHAPTER 3

Modern separation techniques

Until comparatively recently, four general methods were available for separating the rare earth elements. Group methods had been developed for separating light from heavy earth fractions, and precipitation methods, depending on charge change, had been perfected for isolating cerium and europium. Amalgam extraction methods had also been developed for the isolation of samarium, europium, and ytterbium. But the only ways of obtaining the remaining elements in a pure state relied entirely on fractional crystallisation processes. Although these various approaches had provided effective means of dealing with the light earth elements, they were much less effective when applied to the isolation of the heavy earth elements in a pure state and, indeed, this remained a formidable task.

However, the situation has been completely changed by the application of two recently developed techniques, namely, ion-exchange chromatography and counter-current solvent extraction. The newer methods will be described here, together with those of the older ones that still have practical significance.

SULPHATE SEPARATION

Rare-earth sulphates form double salts with alkali metal sulphates, which are salted out by the addition of an excess of alkali sulphate. The sulphates also have a negative temperature coefficient of solubility. Both properties can be exploited for making a rapid light earth–heavy earth separation. In the first method, sodium sulphate is stirred into a cold solution of lanthanide sulphates until the double sulphates of the light earths are precipitated. The process may be controlled spectrophotometrically. The filtrate contains most of the heavy earths and yttrium. Alternatively, when saturated rare earth sulphate solutions are heated, light earth sulphates are the first to crystallise, and may be filtered off. Both these methods, although rapid, effect only crude separations.

EXPLOITATION OF CHARGE CHANGE

Cerium. This element is unique among the lanthanide elements in forming a stable quadripositive ion in aqueous solution. The stable form of the oxide also has the element in this charge state. These properties can both be exploited to give a ready separation from the rest of the lanthanides which all display a very stable terpositive state.

In solution, the salts of the Ln^{3+} ions are resistant to hydrolysis but the ceric ion hydrolyses readily. The solubility product of the hydroxides $Ln(OH)_3$ vary from lanthanum (log $K_{so} = -19.0$) to lutetium (log $K_{so} = -23.7$), quite different from that of ceric hydroxide which has been estimated at log $K_{so} = -51$.[1,2] When cerous solutions are oxidised to the ceric state, for example with chlorine or a bromate, basic ceric salts are precipitated.[3,4] Alternatively, when a mixture of tervalent hydroxides is precipitated, and the product dried, the cerous hydroxide present is oxidised to the ceric state and remains insoluble when the solid is leached with dilute acids.[5,6]

These methods are valuable, since cerium is a major constituent of the rare earths derived from monazite (usually about 50%), and although neither method gives a complete separation, 99% of the cerium can be eliminated in one operation.

Europium. Except for promethium, europium is the least abundant lanthanide element. It has a well defined bipositive state, the redox potential of the Eu^{3+}/Eu^{2+} couple being 0.43 V. The europous ion is moderately stable in water, europous sulphate being sparingly soluble and isomorphous with barium sulphate.[7,8]

References p. 40

Aqueous solutions of certain lanthanides are reduced by zinc, and in the presence of controlled amounts of sulphate ions, europous sulphate is precipitated. In the treatment of low grade materials, it is convenient to co-precipitate barium sulphate as a carrier. Recoveries of 80% have been obtained from materials containing only 0.1% Eu_2O_3.[9] Europium is recovered from the precipitate by leaching with an oxidising agent, and final purification is effected by salting-out the dichloride with cold concentrated hydrochloric acid.[8]

ION-EXCHANGE CHROMATOGRAPHY

This is now the most efficient means available for separating the rare earth elements in a pure state, and may be used for any of the lanthanides. Highly successful methods, in which elution is used,[10,11] have been developed for the separation and identification of fission-product rare earths. These methods are described and discussed in Chapter 10 (p. 121).

Two other chromatographic techniques have been examined for the separation of the rare earths on a large scale. The method of frontal analysis depends on differences in the affinity of ions in solution for the substrate. Thus when a solution containing a mixture of ions of the same charge is passed through a cation-exchange column, the initial fraction in the eluate contains pure A, provided the affinity of ion A for the substrate is less than that of ion B (Fig. 7).

As might be expected, there is comparatively little separation of the rare-earth elements by this means, even when very long resin columns are employed, simply because the affinities of these cations for the resin are so similar.[12,13] However, the important observation was made that the presence of a complexing agent, such as citric acid, in the solution gave improved separation; the separation is, however, in the opposite sense to the one expected in absence of the complexing agent.[14] Later work showed that an essential requirement in obtaining successful separations is for the rare-

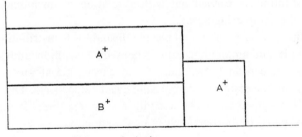

Volume of eluate

Fig. 7. Frontal analysis.

earth cations to have different affinities for the complexing agent.[15]

The type of chromatography known as "displacement development" is used in preparative work. In its simplest form a mixture of ions are exchanged on an ion-exchange material and displaced from it by an ion with a greater affinity for the resin. This gives rise to a development chromatogram, which is characterised by an eluate of constant concentration. The ions are forced down the development column, in order of increasing affinity for the resin. The mixture is resolved into zones containing pure substances, each having an overlap with the zones of the leading and following ion (Fig. 8).

Some sophistication is required to achieve this with the rare earth elements, and in actual practice the lanthanides are eluted from a column in order of decreasing affinity for the complexing

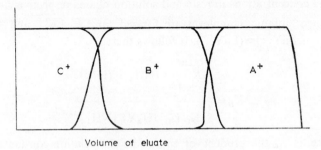

Volume of eluate

Fig. 8. Displacement development.

agent. Elution is carried out with a solution of an ammonium salt of the complexing agent.

In the presence of a complexing ligand, the distribution of lanthanide and ammonium cations between a solution and a cation-exchange resin is the sum of two effects, the affinity of the cations for the resin and complexing agent respectively. Distribution of lanthanide cations between the resin phase (barred) and the aqueous phase (unbarred) is given by the equation:

$$Ln^{3+} + 3\ NH_4^+ \rightleftharpoons \overline{3\ NH_4^+} + Ln^{3+} \tag{1}$$

and the relative affinity of the competing ions is defined as:

$$K \begin{smallmatrix} Ln^{3+} \\ \\ NH_4^+ \end{smallmatrix} = \frac{(NH_4^+)^3\ \overline{(Ln^{3+})}}{\overline{(NH_4^+)^3}\ (Ln^{3+})} \tag{2}$$

Complexing of metal ions by the reagent, for instance EDTA (ethylenediaminetetraacetic acid), is controlled by the reaction:

$$Ln^{3+} + Y^{4-} \rightleftharpoons LnY^{1-} \tag{3}$$

which is defined by the association constant of the cation for the ligand

$$K_C = \frac{LnY^{1-}}{(Ln^{3+})\ (Y^{4-})} \tag{4}$$

Distribution of the metal ion between the two phases is given by the distribution factor $K_D = M_R/M_S$, where M_R and M_S are the metal concentrations in resin and solution phases respectively.

When anionic complexes are formed, $M_R = \overline{Ln^{3+}}$ and M_S $(Ln^{3+} + LnY^{1-}) \approx (LnY^{1-})$. It follows that:

$$K_D = \frac{K \begin{smallmatrix} Ln^{3+} \\ \\ NH_4^+ \end{smallmatrix} (NH_4^+)^3 (H^+)^4}{K_C\ K_a\ (H_4Y)\ (NH_4)^3} \tag{5}$$

where is K_a the product of the acidic dissociation constants of EDTA, the complexing agent. For a pair of rare earth elements in the same solution, the resin affinity terms are similar, hence the separation factor K_S is simply

$$K_S = K_{D1}/K_{D2} = K_{C2}/K_{C1} \qquad (6)$$

that is, the ratio of the association constants of the two ions for the ligand. Eqn. (6) predicts that the lanthanide element with the highest affinity for the complexing agent will tend to pass into the solution phase, and will therefore elute first from an ion-exchange column. Similarly, the elution of mixtures of terpositive ions will generally follow the sequence of their individual affinity for the complexing agent. However, when ions of differing charge are present, the expressions for the distribution factors (K_D) differ in the terms contributed by the affinity of metal ions for the resin. In these circumstances the elution sequence of a series of metals will depend on the eluant concentration.

In practice, two separate cation-exchange columns are usually employed. The first column is loaded with the mixture of rare-earth elements, while various loadings have been proposed for the second (development) column. After loading, the two columns are coupled together and eluted with a complexing agent solution. To obtain separations by the displacement technique, it is essential to secure a complete reflux of lanthanide ions on the development column between the aqueous and resin phases. The loading selected for the development column depends on two properties of the complexing, agent, namely, its solubility in the free acid form and the solubility of its lanthanide anionic complexes.

H^+-*form development columns*. The use of such columns is restricted to conditions in which the complexing agent is water soluble. Citric acid was employed in the first successful method.[16] Coupled ion-exchange columns were eluted with dilute (0.005 M) solutions of triammonium citrate. Anionic complexes are formed on elution:

$$\overline{\text{Ln}^{3+}} + 3\,\text{NH}_4{}^+ \rightarrow \text{Ln}^{3+} + 3\,\overline{\text{NH}_4^+} \qquad (7)$$

$$\text{Ln}^{3+} + 2\,\text{Cit}^{3-} \rightleftharpoons \text{Ln}(\text{Cit})_2^{3-} \qquad (8)$$

When the citrate complexes met the development column,

hydrogen ions were displaced from the resin. These broke down the complex with the result that lanthanide cations were exchanged to the resin phase while citric acid entered the eluate.

$$Ln(Cit)_2^{3-} + \overline{6\,H^+} \rightarrow \overline{Ln^{3+}} + 2\,H_3Cit \tag{9}$$

When the rare earth ions have differing affinities for the citrate ligand, separation takes place in the lanthanide band thus:

$$Ln_a(Cit)_2^{3+} + \overline{Ln_b^{3+}} \rightarrow Ln_b(Cit)_2^{3+} + \overline{Ln_a^{3+}} \tag{10}$$

This effect is integrated by the movement of the band down the column, the separation factors and column length required to separate a pair of elements being inter-related.

The method is effective for separating the light and heavy earth groups (La–Sm and Er–Lu) from each other. However, as the citrate complexes are sparingly soluble in water, and the eluant concentration is near to this limit, the method is very tedious. Also, in the early stages of elution, complexes of the type $Ln(Ln(Cit)_2)$ are formed which, although they supersaturate readily, are very insoluble in water.

The amino-carboxylic acid, β-hydroxyethylethylenediamine triacetic acid (HEEDTA), is soluble in water, and has association constants for the rare-earth elements which make it suitable for separating the La–Sm and Er–Lu groups.[17] Thus it may be used in place of citric acid, but when hydrogen ions are displaced from the development column, the acid forms a salt with the resin.[17,23] This salt of the amino-acid forms a band that moves down the development column in front of the rare earth band. Although the acid is difficult to precipitate in the presence of electrolytes it tends to be precipitated on ion-exchange columns at eluant concentrations above 0.025 M.

Metal-loaded development columns. This method may be used with complexing agents that are insoluble in the free-acid form. EDTA is a convenient reagent for this purpose as its association constants with the rare earth cations vary in a regular manner with atomic number, there being an increase from lanthanum to lutetium.[18] A variety of metal ions have been proposed for loading the development column, *e.g.* Fe^{3+}, Cu^{2+}, Zn^{2+}, of which copper is the one most commonly used.[19,20,21] Careful control of the eluant composition is needed, and the triammonium salt is normally employed. This forms acidic complexes on elution:

$$\overline{Ln^{3+}} + (NH_4)_3HY \rightarrow \overline{3\,NH_4^+} + HLnY \tag{11}$$

$$\overline{3\,Cu^{2+}} + 2(NH_4)_3HY \rightarrow \overline{6NH_4^+} + 2\,HCu_{0.5}(CuY) \tag{12}$$

Under these conditions, an acidic lanthanide complex is formed, and the copper complex contains some cationic metal. At a higher eluant stoicheiometry, lanthanide or metal cation–anion salts such as $Ln(LnY)_3$ or $Cu(CuY)$ are formed, which tend to hydrolyse or be precipitated on the columns, whereas at lower stoicheiometry, EDTA acid is precipitated on the lanthanide column.[22] This disadvantage restricts the use of the method, and in large-scale work a relatively-low (0.015 M) eluant concentration is recommended.[23]

When the method is modified by making a controlled addition of the non-complexing ammonium ion to both rare-earth- and metal-loaded columns, ammonium salts of the lanthanide– or metal-anionic complexes are formed on elution. Separation takes place by ligand exchange on the development column, and the difficulties associated with high metal-ion concentrations are overcome; the eluant concentration may be as high as 0.05 M.[24] For effecting a rapid preliminary group separation of the rare-earth elements, $Ln^{3+}-NH_4^+$ columns without a development column have been successfully used at an eluant concentration of 0.1 M.[25]

A limitation on the ion-exchange technique is imposed by the rate of diffusion of cations within the resin phase, which is lower than that found[26] in water by a factor of from 10^2 to 10^3. To obtain separations, it is essential to have an effective reflux of ions between the resin and solution phases. It is possible to increase the diffusion rates by using resins of lower cross-linkage, and this is feasible for small-scale operations such as fission product separations (p. 121). However, the large volume changes of these resins with alteration in ionic strength prevents their use for large-scale work. To obtain highly pure lanthanides, it is necessary to employ low flow rates and use resin of the smallest practicable particle size.

SOLVENT EXTRACTION

This method may be employed for separating all of the rare earth elements, although it seems to have been used on a macroscopic scale only with the light and middle earth elements. Separation factors between adjacent terpositive lanthanide ions vary from 1.5 to 2.5, depending upon the system. Solvent-extraction systems require one unit, for instance, mixer–settler, per theoretical stage and do not have the integrating effect of a chromatographic column; therefore many stages are essential.

The separation factors between quadripositive and bipositive lanthanide ions and the terpositive ions are much larger, and this has been applied successfully to the purification of cerium and europium. Solvent extractants of current interest are the tri-alkyl phosphates and the alkylated phosphoric acids.

Terpositive lanthanides. For the separation of these ions three systems have been studied in some detail: tri-*n*-butyl phosphate (TBP) suitable for neutral lanthanide nitrates; TBP suitable for lanthanide nitrate–nitric acid; and dialkyl phosphate suitable for lanthanide nitrate–nitric acid.

Neutral lanthanide nitrates are extracted from aqueous solution by TBP in the form of tri-solvates with the structure $Ln(NO_3)_3$. 3 TBP.[27] When concentrated lanthanide nitrate solutions are used, or salting-in agents such as calcium or aluminium nitrates are added to the lanthanide nitrate solution, the organic phase approaches the limiting composition of the tri-solvate. For the light earths (La–Sm), separation factors between individual lanthanides increase with the saturation of the organic phase. Few quantitative data are available, but it appears that separation factors between adjacent rare earths approach a limiting value of from 1.5 to 2.0. The separation of the light earth elements is thus feasible provided sufficient stages are used.[28] No comparable information on the separation of heavy earth elements is available.

In the presence of nitric acid the system becomes more complex. The solvent forms the compound $TBP.HNO_3$ with nitric acid, and, when the nitric acid concentration is greater than 7 N, more than the stoicheiometric quantity of nitric acid is found in the organic phase.[29] These compounds compete with the lanthanide nitrates for the solvent. Thus the partition of lanthanides between the aqueous and organic phases depends on the relative concentrations of the lanthanide salt and nitric acid in the solution. In solutions with acid concentrations below 4 N, partition coefficient–atomic number plots showed an inversion at the mid-point of the series. However, at very high acid concentrations (15 N–18 N), a linear relationship was approached with separation factors for adjacent lanthanide elements of 2.0–2.5.[30, 31] The position of yttrium in the series depended upon the concentration of nitric acid in the aqueous phase. The method has been used to obtain gadolinium concentrates.[32] For this the initial material was dissolved in 13 N nitric acid, and, after countercurrent extraction with the solvent, the Gd_2O_3 content increased from 25% to > 95%.

The dialkyl phosphoric acids are normally used in solution in an inert diluent such as kerosene. As a class, these reagents are frequently referred to as liquid cation-exchangers, since metal ions in solution exchange with ions in the organic phase. Partition coefficients of lanthanides vary with the cube of the concentration of phosphate ester in the organic phase, and inversely with the cube of the hydrogen ion concentration in the aqueous phase. For trace quantities of lanthanides, the variation of partition coefficient with atomic number is linear and the average separation factor between the individual lanthanide elements is 2.5.[33]

For separations which require a heavy loading of the organic phase, such as the separation of large quantities of lanthanides, dialkyl phosphates have the disadvantage of forming hydrogen-bonded dimers in organic solvents; when more than one-sixth of the exchangeable groups have been exchanged for multivalent cations, gelation occurs.[34] Empirical ways of getting round this difficulty have sometimes been found by adding phase modifiers which are usually long-chain aliphatic alcohols.

Extraction of cerium. WARF showed that both nitromethane and TBP were satisfactory for the extraction of the ceric ion from aqueous 8–10 N nitric acid which also contained a bromate holding oxidant.[35] The ceric ion was readily back-extracted into an aqueous phase containing a reducing agent. An essentially similar method has been used for the preparation of radiochemically pure cerium.[36]

Dioctylphosphoric acid has also been employed for the purification of cerium.[37] When ceric ions were extracted from 10 N nitric acid solutions containing terpositive lanthanides, the separation factors from the terpositive lanthanide ions were greater than 10^6.

Extraction of bipositive europium. A comparison of the extraction of terpositive lanthanides and alkaline earths by acidic phosphoric and phosphonic esters showed that the terpositive ions were transferred more readily to the organic phase. This suggested that a separation of bipositive europium from terpositive lanthanides should be feasible.

Europium was reduced to Eu^{2+} by Cr^{2+}, prepared *in situ* by reducing Cr^{3+} with a zinc amalgam; this procedure also removed dissolved oxygen from the solution, which is essential with trace quantities of europium. Separation factors of from 10^5 to 10^6 were found for Ln^{3+}/Eu^{2+} when the organic and aqueous phases were di-(2-ethylhexyl) hydrogen phosphate and 0.05 M HCl + 0.01 M Cr^{2+} respectively.

An aqueous solution of rare earths, containing 0.1 % of Eu_2O_3, was extracted with 1.6 M di-(2-ethylhexyl)phosphoric acid to produce a 0.1 M Ln^{3+} solution in the organic phase. The organic phase was then extracted three times with an aqueous solution which contained 0.5 g/l Zn–Hg and was 0.05 M and 0.01 M with respect to HCl and Cr^{2+}. The recovery of europium from the aqueous phase was 90 %, and separation factors from samarium and gadolinium[38] were both greater than 10^5.

AMALGAM EXTRACTION

The extraction of samarium and ytterbium with sodium amalgam from aqueous solutions of lanthanide concentrates was introduced some years ago by MARSH.[39] Since in its original form the method was difficult to control, it has been re-examined as a batch-extraction technique, buffered lanthanide solutions being used to control the reaction of sodium with hydrogen ions. Extraction depended on two factors, the samarium or ytterbium content of the concentrate, and the pH of the solution. Ytterbium alone was extracted from heavy earth concentrates. Samarium was extracted from light earth concentrates with marginal quantities of light earths, but when europium was present it was extracted at the original Eu: Sm ratio.[40]

Europium and samarium amalgams are stripped quantitatively when run through a column of hot acid (80°, 4 N HCl or 10 N HOAc). By counter-flowing lanthanon solution and sodium amalgam in one column and treating the lanthanide amalgam similarly with hot acid in a second column, a continuous extraction process can be operated. From 80% to 90% of the samarium or ytterbium in a lanthanide concentrate was recovered in one operation and the efficiencies of batch and continuous operation were similar.[41]

Seven of the lanthanide elements are extracted from aqueous solutions by alkali–metal amalgams, the La–Nd group, and Sm'Eu and Yb. The last three elements appear to be reduced to bipositive ions before being converted to the metal. It has been suggested that the extraction process is the result of two opposed effects, electrochemical and hydrolytic. Samarium, europium, and ytterbium are probably extracted preferentially from lanthanide concentrates for kinetic reasons.[42]

ION-EXCHANGE MEMBRANES

Some preliminary experiments have been described by BRIL.[43]

The principle of the method is to apply electromigration to partially complexed rare earth solutions. A five-compartment cell was described, the electrode compartments of which were separated by alternating cationic and anionic membranes. The rare-earth–EDTA solution was fed to the centre compartment of the cell and current was passed through the electrode compartments which were continually flushed with buffer solutions to prevent excessive pH changes. Cationic lanthanide ions tend to move from the centre compartment to the cathode compartment, and similarly, anionic lanthanide ions move to the anode compartment. It was also necessary to add a little buffer solution continually to the intermediate compartments of the cell to stabilise the pH; this eliminated the risk of precipitating lanthanide hydroxides or EDTA acid.

Experiments on the separation of La–Nd and La–Pr–Nd mixtures, partially complexed with EDTA have been described. The separations obtained agreed with the values calculated from the several association constants of these ions for EDTA. An Nd-Th separation has also been examined; it was a very effective separation since there is a large difference in the association constants with EDTA (10^7), and, moreover, the thorium–EDTA complex has no charge. But the use of multi-compartment cells has not been reported.

CONCLUSIONS

The group separation methods based upon sulphate or double-sulphate precipitation seem unlikely to be supplanted, and the classical procedure for the removal of cerium is undoubtedly very effective. Although the cerium isolated in this way is not pure, further purification may be readily achieved by solvent extraction. The recovery of europium as europous sulphate is also efficient, although, as this is one of the least abundant of the rare earth elements, a preliminary concentration of the element is desirable.

Ion exchange is the most powerful method available for isolating the rare-earth elements in a pure state. With a suitable choice of technique and complexing agent, any of the elements may be isolated. In spite of the disadvantage of being a batch process, it has been operated on a large scale. For isolation of the less abundant elements, rapid concentration may be employed, and it is a simple matter to use the columns for storing concentrates of these elements.

Separation factors of 2–2.5 between adjacent rare-earth elements can be obtained by solvent extraction, but each stage requires one mixer–settler unit and the method does not have the integrating effect of an ion-exchange column. No complete investigation of pulsed solvent-extraction columns has been made, and there is no evidence to show whether the kinetics could be sufficiently rapid to permit the successful operation of such a system. The method can be used for separating the light earth elements, but many stages are required to approach the purity of material isolated by ion-exchange techniques. Rapid heavy earth–yttrium separations also appear feasible. The decision whether or not to employ the technique will depend mainly on the purity specified for the product.

Continuous amalgam extraction is probably the best available method for preparing samarium–europium concentrates and also pure ytterbium. These elements may be concentrated readily by ion-exchange.

It has been shown that ion-exchange membranes can be used for separating the lanthanide elements. Although the method is of interest, since it offers the promise of a continuous process, more experimental work will be required to make an assessment possible. Since the separation factors for a single cell are limited to differences in the complexing constants with individual rare-earth elements, a very large number of stages would be required to isolate pure materials.

REFERENCES

1 *Stability Constants, Part 2: Inorganic Ligands*, The Chemical Society, London, 1957.
2 V. M. TARAYAN and L. A. ELIAZYAN, *Izv. Akad. Nauk Arm. SSR, Ser. Khim. Nauk*, 10 (1957) 189.
3 D. W. PEARCE and J. C. BUTLER, *Inorganic Syntheses*, 2 (1946) 48.
4 R. C. VICKERY, *J. Soc. Chem. Ind.*, 67 (1948) 333; 69 (1950) 122.
5 A. R. Powell and Johnson Matthey & Co, *British Patent 510,198*, 28.7.1939.
6 E. S. PILKINGTON and A. W. WYLIE, *J. Soc. Chem. Ind.*, 66 (1947) 387.
7 H. N. McCOY, *J. Am. Chem. Soc.*, 58 (1936) 1577.
8 H. N. McCOY, *J. Am. Chem. Soc.*, 59 (1937) 1131.
9 H. N. McCOY, *J. Am. Chem. Soc.*, 58 (1936) 2279.
10 B. H. KETELLE and G. E. BOYD, *J. Am. Chem. Soc.*, 69 (1947) 2800.
11 D. H. HARRIS and E. R. TOMPKINS, *J. Am. Chem. Soc.*, 69 (1947) 2792.
12 R. G. RUSSELL and D. W. PEARCE, *J. Am. Chem. Soc.*, 65 (1943) 595.
13 B. A. LISTER and M. L. SMITH, *J. Chem. Soc.*, (1948) 1272.
14 O. ERAMETSA, T. G. SAHAMA and V. KANULA, *Ann. Acad. Sci. Fennicaes*, A57 (1941) 5.
15 E. R. TOMPKINS and S. W. MAYER, *J. Am. Chem. Soc.*, 69 (1947) 2859.
16 F. H. SPEDDING, E. I. FULMER, J. E. POWELL, T. A. BUTLER and I. S. YAFFE, *J. Am. Chem. Soc.*, 73 (1951) 4840.
17 F. H. SPEDDING, J. E. POWELL and E. J. WHEELWRIGHT, *J. Am. Chem. Soc.*,78 (1956) 34.
18 G. SCHWARZENBACH, R. GUT and G. ANDREGG, *Helv. Chim. Acta*, 37 (1954) 937.
19 F. H. SPEDDING, J. E. POWELL and E. J. WHEELWRIGHT, *J. Am. Chem. Soc.*, 76 (1954) 612.
20 F. H. SPEDDING, J. E. POWELL and E. J. WHEELWRIGHT, *J. Am. Chem. Soc.*, 76 (1954) 2557.
21 P. KRUMHOLZ, K. BRIL, S. BRIL et al., *Proc. Sec. U.N. Conf. Atomic Energy, Geneva*, 28 (1958) 184.
22 J. K. MARSH, *J. Chem. Soc.*, (1957) 978.
23 F. H. SPEDDING and J. E. POWELL, *Chem. Eng. Progr., Symposium Series (No. 24)*, 55 (1959) 101.
24 F. H. HOWIE and N. E. TOPP, unpublished work.
25 N. E. TOPP and D. D. YOUNG, *British Patent 880,561*, 1961.
26 G. E. BOYD and B. A. SOLDANO, *J. Am. Chem. Soc.* 75 (1953) 6091.
27 E. HESFORD, E. E. JACKSON and H. A. C. McKAY, *J. Inorg. Nucl. Chem.*, 9 (1959) 279.
28 J. BOCHINSKI, M. SMUTZ and F. H. SPEDDING, *Ind. Eng. Chem.*, 50 (1958) 157.
29 D. F. PEPPARD, G. W. MASON and J. L. MAIER, *J. Inorg. Nucl. Chem.*, 3 (1956) 215.
30 D. SCARGILL, K. ALCOCK, J. M. FLETCHER, E. HESFORD and H. A. C. McKAY, *J. Inorg. Nucl. Chem.*, 4 (1957) 304.

31 D. F. PEPPARD, W. J. DRISCOLL, R. J. SIRONEN and S. McCARTY, *J. Inorg. Nucl. Chem.*, 4 (1957) 326.
32 B. WEAVER, F. A. KAPPELMANN and A. C. TOPP, *J. Am. Chem. Soc.*, 75 (1953) 3943.
33 D. F. PEPPARD, G. W. MASON, J. L. MAIER and W. J. DRISCOLL, *J. Inorg. Nucl. Chem.*, 4 (1957) 334.
34 D. P. PEPPARD, J. W. FERRARO and G. W. MASON, *J. Inorg. Nucl. Chem.*, 4 (1957) 371.
35 J. C. WARF, *J. Am. Chem. Soc.*, 71 (1949) 3257.
36 H. W. KIRBY, *Anal. Chem.*, 29 (1957) 1599.
37 D. F. PEPPARD, G. W. MASON and S. W. MOLINE, *J. Inorg. Nucl. Chem.*, 5 (1957) 141.
38 D. F. PEPPARD, E. P. HORWITZ and G. W. MASON, *J. Inorg. Nucl. Chem.*, 24 (1962) 429.
39 J. K. MARSH, *J. Chem. Soc.*, (1942) 398, 523; (1943) 8, 531.
40 M. F. BARRETT, D. SWEASEY and N. E. TOPP, *J. Inorg. Nucl. Chem.*, 24 (1962) 571.
41 M. F. BARRETT and N. E. TOPP, *J. Appl. Chem.*, 13 (1963) 7.
42 M. F. BARRETT, D. SWEASEY and N. E. TOPP, *J. Inorg. Nucl. Chem.*, 25 (1963) 1273.
43 K. BRIL, S. BRIL and P. KRUMHOLZ, *J. Phys. Chem.*, 63 (1959) 256.

CHAPTER 4

Salts of the rare earth elements

The compounds here considered are mainly those soluble in water or other solvent, or stable in the presence of water. Most of them are prepared by reactions in solution from which the compound emerges as a solute or precipitate. The most important intermediates in these preparations are the oxides which are made by ignition of the oxalates. The carbonates or hydroxides can also be used, and are more convenient for some purposes than the non-stoicheiometric Pr or Tb oxides when the anion is prone to oxidation. The evidence is that terpositive rare-earth salts are not hydrolysed to an appreciable extent in solution.

SALTS OF TERPOSITIVE LANTHANIDES

Nitrates. These are prepared by the reaction of nitric acid with a small excess of the oxide, which is removed by filtration when the reaction is complete. The salts crystallise as the hexahydrates, $Ln(NO_3)_3.6H_2O$, which are all very soluble in water ($> 2\ M$ at $25°$). They are also soluble in alcohol and acetone. When heated at about $850°$, they release oxygen and oxides of nitrogen and leave the lanthanide oxide.

Halides. The chlorides, bromides and iodides are similarly prepared by treating the oxide with the appropriate halogen acid. These salts crystallise as hexahydrates which are very soluble in water. On the other hand, the fluorides are very insoluble; when hydrofluoric acid is added to a lanthanide solution (say the nitrate) a gelatinous precipitate forms which coarsens when heated to give the hemi-hydrate, $LnF_3.0.5H_2O$.

The halides hydrolyse readily on evaporation in solution and produce oxide halides.

$$LnX_3 + H_2O \rightarrow LnOX + 2\,HX \qquad (1)$$

The oxide halides are very insoluble in water and alcohol, and thus provide a very sensitive test for hydrolysis. The hydrated fluorides also hydrolyse on heating, in part being converted into oxide fluorides. Dry routes are used for the preparation of the anhydrous halides, which are important intermediates in the preparation of the lanthanide metals (p. 125).

Crystal structures of a number of rare earth chlorides have been determined and shown to be monoclinic.[1,2] The fluorides, oxide fluorides and oxide chlorides have also been examined.[3,4,5]

Oxohalide salts. The perchlorates are prepared from the oxide and perchloric acid. They are very soluble in water and form deliquescent crystals of composition $Ln(ClO_4)_3.9H_2O$. Bromates are prepared by double decomposition of a lanthanide sulphate and barium bromate. The barium sulphate is removed by filtration and the lanthanide bromate crystallised from the filtrate. The iodates are sparingly soluble in water and may be prepared by double decomposition.

Sulphates. Anhydrous sulphates result when the oxides are heated with a small excess of concentrated sulphuric acid, and the temperature is raised to 400°–500° to decompose acid sulphates. Above 1000° the sulphates pyrolyse and leave the corresponding oxides.

The anhydrous sulphates are hygroscopic solids, which dissolve in water with the evolution of heat. Octahydrates are crystallised from aqueous solution. At 20°, the solubilities of the sulphates decrease regularly from lanthanum to europium, and then increase again.[6] The sulphates have a negative temperature coefficient of solubility. This property can be exploited to effect a rapid separation of the light and heavy earths, since the light earth sulphates are less soluble when heated.

Sulphites. These are sparingly soluble in water, and may be prepared by double decomposition. Alternatively, sulphur dioxide can be passed through a dilute suspension of the carbonate or oxide

and crystalline salts be produced by concentrating the solution.
Thiosulphates. Double decomposition reactions are used for their
preparation. The salts are readily soluble in water and may be
crystallised.

Selenates. The oxide is dissolved in selenic acid to form the
hydrated salt, $Ln_2(SeO_4)_3.8H_2O$, which is crystallised from solution.

Carbonates. These are precipitated when a slight excess of ammonium carbonate is added to a dilute solution of a lanthanide
salt. The gelatinous precipitate coarsens when heated. The salts
are trihydrates, and on heating to 900° they pyrolyse to the oxides.

Hydroxides. The addition of ammonia or an alkali to a hot
solution of a lanthanide salt (with one exception) precipitates the
hydroxide. The gelatinous material is coarsened by being kept in
the hot solution. When heated above 200°, the hydroxide $Ln(OH)_3$
is dehydrated to the oxide hydroxide $LnO.(OH)$ which has been
characterised by X-ray techniques.[7]

Cerium is the single exception to the general rule. Cerous
hydroxide is unstable and can only be prepared by rigorously
excluding air. It is oxidised slowly on standing in air or more
rapidly on drying, being converted eventually to the yellow ceric
hydroxide. The oxidation is rapid when it is precipitated in the
presence of a hypochlorite or hypobromite. Owing to the ease
with which it is oxidised, cerous hydroxide is a powerful reducing
agent.

Oxalates. The normal oxalates may be prepared by homogenous
precipitation from neutral solution by the hydrolysis of methyl
oxalate under reflux conditions. Oxalates of the light earths and
yttrium crystallise as decahydrates, but those of the heavy earths
are less heavily hydrated. The lanthanum salt has a monoclinic
structure.

For preparative or analytical purposes, oxalic acid or ammonium
oxalate are preferred as precipitants. If the lanthanide salt solution
is not strongly acidic ($< N$) and the final pH is adjusted to 2 with
ammonia after addition of the reagent, the light earths and yttrium
produce normal oxalates but the heavy earth precipitates are mix-

tures of the normal oxalates and the double ammonium oxalate NH_4LnOx_2.[9]

All the oxalates are very insoluble in water itself, the solubility products[10] being of the order of 10^{-30}. On heating in air to 800–900° both normal and double ammonium oxalates decompose to the oxides. A platinum container should be used for the ignition as the rare-earth oxides will react with silica containers at this temperature to form silicates. The oxalates are decomposed to hydroxides when boiled with a slight excess of alkali.

Chromates. The salts are sparingly soluble in water and are prepared by double decomposition of a soluble salt with potassium chromate. The octahydrates, $Ln_2(CrO_4)_3.8H_2O$, are isomorphous with the sulphates.

Molybdates and tungstates. Both of these are sparingly soluble in water and are prepared by double decomposition with sodium molybdate or tungstate.

Phosphates. The phosphates are precipitated when sodium phosphate is added to a lanthanide salt solution of pH 4.5. Pyrophosphates have been prepared in a similar manner. The salts have the compositions $LnPO_4$ and $Ln_4(P_2O_7)_3$ respectively. Stable complexes are formed in solution with pyrophosphate and polyphosphate ions.[11,12]

Borates. These separate when ammonium borate is added to a neutral lanthanide nitrate solution. The product is heated to 1400° to volatilise any excess of boric oxide, and has the composition $LnBO_3$. Alternatively, stoicheiometric quantities of the two oxides are heated together at 1000–1200°. The crystal structures of a number of these compounds have been determined.[13,14,15] When the oxides are heated with an excess of boric oxide, two liquid layers separate; the lower layer contains the lanthanon salt.

Silicates. These are prepared by heating together a rare-earth oxide and silica. If an excess of silica is present, two liquid layers separate.[16] The compounds $Ln_2O_3.SiO_2$ and $Ln_2O_3.3SiO_2$ have been identified in the reaction products at 1200–1400° and pyrosilicates are formed above 1500°.[17,18] Phase diagrams have been produced for a number of these systems.

DOUBLE SALTS

Nitrates. Double salts are formed with nitrates with both uni- and bipositive cations. Salts formed by the interaction of lanthanide salts with alkali nitrates have the composition $Ln(NO_3)_3.2NH_4NO_3.4H_2O$; the salts in which a bipositive metal ion is present are more heavily hydrated, such as $2 Ln(NO_3)_3.3 Mg(NO_3)_2.24 H_2O$.

Sulphates. Double sulphates are formed with alkali metal sulphates, and salts with a variety of compositions have been isolated. It appears that these systems reach equilibrium very slowly.[10] A typical double salt has the composition $Ln_2(SO_4)_3.Na_2SO_4.8 H_2O$. The salts are of considerable practical importance because differences in their solubilities make possible a rough group separation of the light and heavy earth elements. For instance after decomposing the source mineral by acid attack, acidic rare earth sulphate solutions are obtained. By the addition of sodium sulphate or chloride to a cold solution of mixed sulphates, double sulphates of the light earths are precipitated while the heavy earth salts remain in solution.[20, 21]

Cyanides. Simple cyanides of the rare earths have not been prepared in aqueous media, as the metal hydroxides are precipitated through hydrolysis. However, a number of complex cyanides are known. The cyanoferrates(III), $LnFe(CN)_6.5H_2O$ are well defined compounds that can be purified by crystallisation. Double alkali cyanoferrates(II) such as $KLnFe(CN)_6.xH_2O$ have been prepared. A series of heavily hydrated cyanoplatinates(II) $Ln_2[Pt(CN)_4]_3.20H_2O$ are well defined crystalline compounds. Cyanocobaltates (III) and cyanonickelates(II) have also been made.

Oxalates. Double ammonium oxalates are precipitated from rare earth salt solutions by oxalate reagents from strongly acidic solutions.[9] Similar compounds with alkali metals, the salts $KSmOx_2$ and $NaLaOx_2$, have also been reported, although they have not been investigated systematically. They were prepared by precipitation with concentrated solutions of the alkali oxalates.[22] The formation of such salts seems a likely explanation of the retention of alkali metals by rare earth oxalate precipitates. *Carbonates.* Double salts of the general formula, $Ln_2(CO_3)_3$ $Na_2CO_3.xH_2O$, are formed with alkali metal carbonates. They are prepared by adding a lanthanide salt to a concentrated solution of alkali carbonate.

SALTS WITH ORGANIC ACIDS

Acetates and formates. The oxide or carbonate is heated with the appropriate acid. The salts have no tendency to hydrolyse; they crystallise readily from hot solutions and are moderately soluble in water at room temperature.

Ethyl sulphates. Barium ethyl sulphate and a lanthanide sulphate, in stoicheiometric proportions, react to form these compounds. Alternatively, they may be prepared by double decomposition between a lanthanide chloride and sodium sulphate, in alcohol. The salts form an isomorphous series of composition $Ln(EtSO_4)_3$. $9 H_2O$.

Dimethyl phosphates. These are formed by the reaction of oxide or carbonate with dimethyl phosphoric acid. They are anhydrous and have a negative temperature coefficient of solubility.[23]

Miscellaneous. In the search for salts of use in separations by fractional crystallisation a very wide range of organic salts has been investigated. The malonates, glycollates, sebacates, cacodylates, and numerous derivatives of benzene sulphonic acid have been prepared. Complex salts with the organic base antipyrene have also been examined; the iodides crystallise readily.[24]

CERIC COMPOUNDS

Studies of the Ce^{4+}/Ce^{3+} potential, and the solution chemistry of some ceric systems, show that solutions of ceric salts are complex; both hydrolysed and polynuclear species are present in solution, and the concentration of the quadripositive ion is probably very low (p. 56). Owing to hydrolysis, solutions of ceric salts are strongly acidic, and they are hydrolysed readily to precipitate basic salts. In consequence, relatively few ceric salts have been prepared in a pure condition.

Double nitrates. Pure ceric nitrate, $Ce(NO_3)_4$, has not been obtained. However, double nitrates are formed with unipositive and bipositive metals, such as $Ce(NO_3)_4.2NH_4NO_3$ and $Ce(NO_3)_4.Mg(NO_3)_2$. The important ammonium salt is prepared by the electrolytic oxidation of the corresponding cerous salt.

Ceric sulphate. Ceric oxide is heated with concentrated sulphuric acid; the insoluble salt is removed by filtration, washed with acetic acid, and dried. The salt is soluble in water, giving unstable solutions which are stabilised by the addition of sulphuric acid. Double sulphates are obtained by concentrating acidic solutions of ceric sulphate and alkali sulphates. The ammonium salt, which is an important analytical reagent, has the composition $Ce(SO_4)_2.2(NH_4)_2SO_4.2H_2O$.

Ceric iodate. The salt is precipitated by the addition of an iodate to a strongly-acidic solution of a ceric salt.

Halides. The chloride, $CeCl_4$, has not been isolated. Ceric hydroxide dissolves in concentrated hydrochloric acid with the evolution of chlorine, and the product is cerous chloride.

Double salts of ceric chloride, however, have been prepared by dissolving ceric hydroxide in methanol solutions of hydrochloric acid, and adding an organic base. The pyridine salt has the composition $CeCl_4.2C_5H_5N.HCl$.

The hydrated fluoride $CeF_4.H_2O$ is precipitated by treating ceric hydroxide with hydrofluoric acid. As this salt is hydrolysed when heated, dry routes are used for the preparation of CeF_4. This product is obtained by treating cerous chloride or fluoride with fluorine at 200°.[25,26]

Ceric hydroxide. When a ceric salt solution is treated with an alkali, basic salts are precipitated. A convenient preparative method is, however, to precipitate ceric ammonium nitrate from a cold solution with ammonia; repeated leaching of the precipitate with cold water yields a product with the composition $2CeO_2.3H_2O$.

An alternative way is by the precipitation of a cerous salt with ammonia in the presence of hydrogen peroxide; when the mixture is boiled, the red-brown precipitate is converted to ceric hydroxide. *Oxidation and reduction of cerium compounds.* The measured potential of the Ce^{4+}/Ce^{3+} couple is known to vary with the concentration and nature of the anion in solution, and values between 1.87 and 1.28 V have been reported (p. 59). Powerful oxidising agents are therefore needed to bring about the cerous–ceric oxidation. In acidic solution, this is effected by treatment with persulphate or sodium bismuthate; electrolytic oxidation can also be used. In alkaline solutions, potassium permanganate, hypochlorites or hypobromites effect the oxidation. A variety of reagents reduce ceric salts. Of these, hydrogen peroxide or hydroxylamine are probably the most convenient laboratory reagents. As ceric oxalate is unstable, reduction is readily obtained by adding oxalic acid to a hot acid solution of a ceric salt; cerous oxalate is precipitated.

SALTS OF BIPOSITIVE LANTHANIDES

Owing to the instability of their bipositive ions in aqueous solution, dry routes are used for preparing many of these lanthanide compounds. However, some salts of bivalent samarium and europium have been prepared by reactions in solution.

Europium. Bipositive europium is conveniently prepared by reducing the terpositive lanthanide ions in a Jones reductor. The bipositive chloride, fluoride, sulphate, carbonate, oxalate, and hydroxide have been prepared by wet reactions.[27]

Samarium. Samarous chloride may be prepared by reduction of the trichloride with magnesium in an alcohol solution of hydrochloric acid. The bipositive fluoride and hydroxide have been prepared in non-aqueous solutions.[28]

ORGANIC COMPOUNDS

Acetylacetonates. A neutral lanthanide solution is warmed with an excess of the reagent. The lanthanide solution is buffered, or a gradual addition of ammonia is made to keep the solution neutral. The compounds have the composition $Ln(C_5H_8O_2)_3$. They crystallise from alcohol, benzene or chloroform, and are sparingly soluble in water; they melt with decomposition.

Alkoxides. A number of lanthanide alkoxides have been prepared by the reaction of the chloride dissolved in methanol with a solution of lithium methoxide.

$$LnCl_3 + 3MeOLi \rightarrow Ln(OMe)_3 + 3LiCl. \qquad (2)$$

Higher alkoxides are prepared from the methoxy derivatives by alcohol-exchange reactions; the product is isolated after removal of the methanol by azeotropic distillation with benzene.[29, 30]

Compounds of quadripositive cerium are prepared by dissolving ceric pyridinium chloride in butanol and passing dry ammonia into the solution.

$$\begin{aligned} CeCl_4.2(C_5H_5N.HCl) + 4BuOH + 6NH_3 \rightarrow \\ Ce(OBu)_4 + 6NH_4Cl + 2C_5H_5N \end{aligned} \qquad (3)$$

Ceric alkoxides of the tertiary alcohols may be distilled or sublimed.[31, 32]

Cyclopentadienides. The anhydrous chlorides, in tetrahydrofurane solution, are caused to react with sodium cyclopentadienide.[33, 34]

$$LnCl_3 + 3C_5H_5Na \rightarrow Ln(C_5H_5)_3 + 3NaCl \qquad (4)$$

Mono- and dicyclopentadienyl chlorides are prepared by similar reactions with either one or two molecular proportions of sodium cyclopentadienide. They are purified by sublimation or crystallisation.[35, 36]

$$LnCl_3 + C_5H_5Na \rightarrow C_5H_5LnCl_2 + NaCl \qquad (5)$$

$$LnCl_3 + 2C_5H_5Na \rightarrow (C_5H_5)_2LnCl + 2NaCl \qquad (6)$$

The cyclopentadienyl compounds are the only known organic derivatives of the lanthanides which have metal–carbon bonds. They are extremely reactive and must be handled in an inert atmosphere. The metal–carbon bond is ionic, since the magnetic susceptibilities of all three types of compound are in excellent agreement with the theoretical values for the terpositive ions. Their solutions have absorption spectra similar to those of aqueous solutions of lanthanide salts. They react readily with ferrous chloride to give ferrocene, and organic substitution reactions are possible on the halide groups of the mono- and dicyclopentadienyl chlorides.

REFERENCES

1 D. H. TEMPLETON and G. F. CARTER, *J. Phys. Chem.*, 58 (1954) 940.
2 D. H. TEMPLETON and C. H. DAUBEN, *J. Am. Chem. Soc.*, 76 (1954) 5237.
3 A. ZALKIN and D. H. TEMPLETON, *J. Am. Chem. Soc.*, 75 (1953) 2453.
4 W. H. ZACHARIASEN, *Acta Cryst.*, 4 (1951) 231.
5 D. H. TEMPLETON and C. H. DAUBEN, *J. Am. Chem. Soc.*, 75 (1953) 6069.
6 K. S. JACKSON and G. RIENACKER, *J. Chem. Soc.*, (1930) 1687.
7 R. FRICKE and A. SEITZ, *Z. Anorg. Chem.*, 254 (1947) 107.
8 V. GILPIN and W. C. MCCRONE, *Anal. Chem.*, 24 (1952) 225.
9 M. F. BARRETT, T. R. R. MCDONALD and N. E. TOPP, *J. Inorg. Nucl. Chem.*, 26 (1964) 931.
10 L. SARVER and P. H. M. BRINTON, *J. Am. Chem. Soc.*, 49 (1927) 943.
11 A. G. BUYERS, E. GIESBRECHT and L. F. AUDRIETH, *J. Inorg. Nucl. Chem.*, 5 (1957) 133.
12 E. GIESBRECHT and L. F. AUDRIETH, *J. Inorg. Nucl. Chem.*, 6 (1958) 308.
13 E. J. FELTEN, *J. Inorg. Nucl. Chem.*, 19 (1961) 61.
14 E. M. LEVIN, R. S. ROTH and J. B. MARTIN, *Am. Mineralogist*, 46 (1961) 1030.
15 R. E. NEWNHAM, M. J. REDMAN and R. P. SANTORO, *J. Am. Ceram. Soc.*, 46 (1963) 253.
16 N. A. TOPOROV and I. A. BONDAR, *Silikat Techn.*, 13 (1962) 137.
17 E. K. KALER, N. A. GADINE and E. P. SAVCHENKO, *Akad. Nauk S.S.S.R.*, (1962) 1728, 1735.
18 N. A. TOPOROV and L. A. BONDAR, *Izv. Akad. Nauk S.S.S.R. Otd. Khim. Nauk*, (1961) 1372.
19 C. JAMES and H. C. HOLDNESS, *J. Am. Chem. Soc.*, 35 (1913) 559.
20 T. MOELLER and H. E. KREMERS, *Ind. Eng. Chem.(Anal. Edn.)*, 17 (1945) 44.
21 J. K. MARSH, *Nature*, 163 (1949) 998.
22 I. M. KOLTHOFF and R. ELMQUIST, *J. Am. Chem. Soc.*, 53 (1931) 1232.

23 J. K. MARSH, *J. Chem. Soc.*, (1939) 554.
24 J. K. MARSH, *J. Chem. Soc.*, (1950) 577.
25 W. KLEMM and P. HENKEL, *Z. Anorg. Allgem. Chem.*, 220 (1934) 180.
26 H. VON WARTENBERG, *Z. Anorg. Allgem. Chem.*, 244 (1940) 339.
27 H. N. McCOY, *J. Am. Chem. Soc.*, 61 (1939) 2456.
28 A. F. CLIFFORD and H. C. BEACHELL, *J. Am. Chem. Soc.*, 70 (1948) 2730.
29 D. C. BRADLEY and M. M. FAKTOR, *Chem. Ind. (London)*, (1958) 1332.
30 D. C. BRADLEY, *Progr. Inorg. Chem.*, 3 (1960) 303.
31 D. C. BRADLEY, A. K. CHATTERJEE and W. WARDLAW, *J. Chem. Soc.*, (1956) 2260.
32 D. C. BRADLEY, A. K. CHATTERJEE and W. WARDLAW, *J. Chem. Soc.*, (1957) 2600.
33 G. WILKINSON and J. M. BIRMINGHAM, *J. Am. Chem. Soc.*, 76 (1954) 6210.
34 J. M. BIRMINGHAM and G. WILKINSON, *J. Am. Chem. Soc.*, 78 (1956) 42.
35 S. MANASTYRSKYJ, R. E. MANGANIN, and M. DUBECK, *Inorg. Chem.*, 2 (1963) 904.
36 R. E. MANGANIN, S. MANASTYSKYJ, and M. DUBECK, *J. Am. Chem. Soc.*, 85 (1963) 672.

CHAPTER 5

Solution chemistry of the rare earth elements

Studies of solutions of the rare earth elements have mainly been confined to those of the Ln^{3+} ions in water. The bipositive ions are insufficiently stable in water to permit investigation by classical techniques. The ceric systems that have been examined quantitatively proved to be complex, and there are indications from other sources that this is general. The salts of the terpositive lanthanides form an interesting group, since their hydrolysis is slight and can be controlled without difficulty. The behaviour of these ions is consistent with a simple picture of an increase in hydration with atomic number, the size of the hydrated ion increasing from lanthanum to lutetium.

ELECTRICAL CONDUCTIVITY

Measurements have been made on dilute solutions of most of the chlorides, and a number of bromides, perchlorates, and nitrates

TABLE 8

LIMITING EQUIVALENT CONDUCTIVITIES OF
TERPOSITIVE IONS AT $25°$

Ion	λ_o	Ion	λ_o	Ion	λ_o
La	69.6	Eu	67.8	Tm	65.4
Ce	69.8	Gd	67.4	Yb	65.4
Pr	69.5	Dy	67.4	Lu	64.7
Nd	69.6	Ho	66.3	Y	64.8
Sm	68.6	Er	65.9		

have also been examined.[1,2,3,4] These salts behave as typical 1 : 3 electrolytes, and obey an extended form of the Onsager equation up to concentrations of 0.01 N. The limiting mobilities of a number of rare earth cations are summarised in Table 8. The lanthanide data were obtained from conductivity measurements on the halide and perchlorate salts. The value for yttrium is probably less accurate since it was derived from measurements on the sulphate.

Solutions of the rare earth sulphates show a behaviour typical of extensive ion-pair formation*. The dissociation constants of a number of the sulphates at 25° varied from 2.2×10^{-4} to 2.6×10^{-4}, the value for yttrium[5,6] being 3.4×10^{-4}.

Few electrolytes of the 3 : 3 valency type have been examined, and among them are the ferricyanides of lanthanum, neodymium, and gadolinium.[7,8] Their dissociation constants in water at 25° are all close to 1.8×10^{-4}. In more concentrated solutions, it has been suggested that the extent of ion-pair formation passes through a minimum.[7] The Bjerrum theory of ion association predicts that the dissociation of symmetrical electrolytes should vary inversely with the dielectric constant of the solvent, that is, the effect is predominantly electrostatic.[9] This relationship has been verified in a range of water–organic solvent mixtures for lanthanum ferricyanide and cobalticyanide.[10,11]

Lanthanum ferrocyanide has been studied by the spectrophotometric technique. Its dissociation constant is 9.0×10^{-6}. An examination by the method of continuous variation showed[12] that the only important ion-pair was the species $LaFe(CN)_6{}^-$.

TRANSPORT NUMBERS

Measurements have been made on a number of chlorides, bromides,

---

* The equivalent conductivity of strong electrolytes, in dilute solution, is linear with the square root of the solution concentration (Debye-Huckel theory). Deviations from the limiting law are explained in terms of ion-pair formation. In the simplest case, when the electrolyte is of a symmetrical valency type, the ion-pair does not contribute to the conductance of the solution, so the conductivity of the solution is lower than predicted by theory.

nitrates and perchlorates by the moving boundary method. The values obtained are linear with the square root of concentration, and approach theoretical behaviour only at very low concentrations. The cation transport numbers for infinite dilution show a general tendency to decrease with atomic number.[4, 13, 14, 15]

ACTIVITY COEFFICIENTS

The activity coefficients of a number of dilute chloride and bromide solutions have been measured in concentration cells with a liquid junction. Over the concentration range 0.005–0.05 M, the experimental results are in good agreement with deductions from the Debye-Huckel theory (Table 9). In this range, the activity coefficients decrease with atomic number as far as dysprosium, and then increase to lutetium.[3, 16, 17]

Measurements have also been made on more concentrated soluti-

TABLE 9

ACTIVITY COEFFICIENTS OF DILUTE SOLUTIONS OF RARE EARTH CHLORIDE

Salt	Concentration, moles/l						
	0.0005	0.001	0.002	0.005	0.01	0.02	0.03
$LaCl_3$	0.8348	0.7758	0.7257	0.6311	0.5557	0.4798	0.4356
$CeCl_3$	0.8353	0.7753	0.7241	0.6303	0.5546	0.4794	0.4364
$PrCl_3$	0.8350	0.7762	0.7263	0.6314	0.5543	0.4792	0.4354
$NdCl_3$	0.8354	0.7765	0.7250	0.6300	0.5488	0.4720	0.4282
$SmCl_3$	0.8346	0.7756	0.7243	0.6301	0.5536	0.4769	0.4330
$EuCl_3$	0.8345	0.7756	0.7243	0.6297	0.5523	0.4759	0.4319
$GdCl_3$	0.8346	0.7757	0.7245	0.6306	0.5527	0.4759	0.4337
$DyCl_3$	0.8336	0.7740	0.7236	0.6363	0.5432	0.4661	0.4232
$HoCl_3$	0.8361	0.7788	0.7289	0.6367	0.5618	0.4854	0.4431
$ErCl_3$	0.8357	0.7783	0.7284	0.6350	0.5597	0.4832	0.4408
$TmCl_3$	0.8329	0.7802	0.7285	0.6345	0.5554	0.4798	0.4378
$YbCl_3$	0.8331	0.7793	0.7281	0.6318	0.5591	0.4834	0.4410
$LuCl_3$	0.8453	0.7808	0.7301	0.6389	0.5647	0.4896	0.4469

ons (0.1—2.0 M) of some of the chlorides by the isopiestic method. Minimum values were found at about 0.4 M, and, as the solutions became more concentrated, there was an increased tendency for the activity coefficients to increase with atomic number.[18]

MISCELLANEOUS PROPERTIES

Densities, apparent molal volumes, and compressibilities of a number of chloride and nitrate solutions have been determined. Heats of solution and dilution of certain of the lanthanide chlorides have also been measured; they increase in a regular manner with atomic number.[19,20,21]

HYDROLYSIS OF THE TERVALENT IONS

Several studies of the hydrolysis of lanthanide(III) salt solutions have been made, from which it appears to be negligible below pH 5.0. The solubility products of the hydroxides increase in a regular sequence from lanthanum (log K_{so}—19.0) to lutetium (log K_{so}—23.7), yttrium (log K_{so}—22.1) appearing in the middle of the rare earth series. The ease of hydrolysis thus increases with the size of the hydrated ion.[22,23,24,25]

BIEDERMANN has found evidence for the formation of the species $LaOH^{2+}$ and $La_2(OH)^{5+}$ in lanthanum solutions at pH 6.5.[26] Under similar conditions, cerium solations contained the $Ce_3(OH)_5^{4+}$ ion, and $Y(OH)^{2+}$ and $Y_2(OH)_2^{4+}$ species were found in yttrium solutions.[26a]

THE NATURE OF CERIC SOLUTIONS

The ceric ion is much more readily hydrolysed than the rare earth 3+ ions. The solubility product of the hydroxide $Ce(OH)_4$ has been determined, log K_{so}—51.[27] Only two studies have been made of the nature of the species in ceric solutions; in both of these spectrophotometric techniques were used, although there is much indirect evidence of hydrolysis and ion-pair formation. In perchlorate solution the following species were identified:

$$Ce^{4+} + H_2O \rightleftharpoons Ce(OH)^{3+} + H^+ \tag{1}$$

$$2 Ce(OH)^{3+} \rightleftharpoons (Ce-O-Ce)^{6+} + H_2O \tag{2}$$

At 25°, the association constants for the two reactions were $K_1 = 5.2$ and $K_2 = 16.5$. Measurements over the temperature range from 5° to 35° enabled the free energy and entropy changes to be determined.[28] In sulphate solutions, evidence was obtained of stepwise ion-association as well as hydrolysis. The following additional species were identified:

$$Ce^{4+} + HSO_4^- \rightleftharpoons CeSO_4^{2+} + H^+ \tag{3}$$

$$CeSO_4^{2+} + HSO_4^- \rightleftharpoons Ce(SO_4)_2 + H^+ \tag{4}$$

$$CeSO_4 + HSO_4^- \rightleftharpoons Ce(SO_4)_2^{2-} + H^+ \tag{5}$$

Association constants for these three reactions were $K_1 = 3500$, $K_2 = 200$, and $K_3 = 20$ respectively.[29]

COMPLEX-ION FORMATION

A number of association constants of individual rare earth ions with organic ligands have been recorded.[30] However, the most extensive series of measurements, frequently including the complete rare earth series, have been made with the aminocarboxylic acids. Some typical results are summarised in Table 10; with the exception of TRILO, all of these ligands form 1 : 1 complexes with the rare earths.

The variation of association constant with ionic size is of considerable theoretical interest, and attempts have been made to measure the heat and entropy of association. For the EDTA complexes, BETTS found an entropy change at 25° of 24 e.u./mole

TABLE 10

ASSOCIATION CONSTANTS OF RARE EARTH CATIONS
WITH AMINOCARBOXYLIC ACIDS

Rare earth element	EDTA log K	TRILO log K_1	TRILO log K_2	HEEDTA log K	DCTA log K	DTPA log K	EGTA log K	EEDTA log K
La	15.50	10.64	7.37	13.22	16.26	19.96	15.84	16.29
Ce	15.98	10.91	7.98	14.08	16.76		16.06	17.13
Pr	16.40	11.04	8.18	14.39	17.31	21.85	16.17	17.61
Nd	16.61	11.22	8.43	14.71	17.68	22.24	16.59	17.81
Sm	17.14	11.29	9.20	15.15	18.38	22.84	17.75	18.25
Eu	17.35	11.36		15.21	18.62	22.91		
Gd	17.37	11.38	9.35	15.10	18.77	23.01	17.50	18.21
Tb	17.93	11.54		15.10	19.50	23.21	17.80	18.31
Dy	18.30	11.65	9.40	15.08	19.69	23.46	17.84	18.29
Ho	18.74	11.79		15.06			17.90	18.17
Er	18.85	11.94		15.17	20.68	23.18	18.00	18.18
Tm	19.32	12.13		15.38	20.96	22.97	17.96	18.01
Yb	19.51	12.29	9.22	15.64	21.12	23.01	18.22	18.06
Lu	19.83	12.44		15.79	21.51		18.48	17.92
Y	18.09	11.33	9.02	14.49	19.15	22.40	17.16	17.79

EDTA Ethylenediaminetetraacetic acid[31]
TRILO Nitrilotriacetic acid[32]
HEEDTA β-Hydroxyethylenediaminetriacetic acid[33]
DCTA, 1:2-diaminocyclohexanetetraacetic acid[31]
DTPA Diethylenetriaminepentaacetic acid[34]
EGTA 1:2-bis(2-di(carboxymethyl)aminoethoxy)ethane[35]
EEDTA 2:2-bis(2-di(carboxymethyl)amino)ethyl ether[35]

from lanthanum to lutetium.[36] MOELLER measured the association constants with DTPA at a range of temperatures and found the change in entropy from La to Lu to be 15 e.u./mole.[37]

Complexing with the acetate ligand has also been examined with a number of the rare earth ions. Four acetate ligands are added stepwise; the association constants do not show any marked trends with atomic number.[38,39]

REDUCTION POTENTIALS

Potentials of the Ln^{3+}/Ln^{2+} couples of Sm, Eu and Yb are 1.35, 0.43 and 1.15 V respectively. The value for europium was established by the use of cells containing known concentrations of the two cationic species in a formate solution.[40] However, it is known that formate ions associate with lanthanide ions, and recently a revised value of 0.35 V for this couple was found in perchlorate solutions.[41] Polarographic methods were used for the other two elements because of the instability of the bipositive ions in water.[42,43]

The potential of the Ce^{4+}/Ce^{3+} couple depends on the anion in solution. The following values were obtained by SMITH and GETZ.[44]

TABLE 11

EFFECT OF ANION ON POTENTIAL OF Ce^{4+}/Ce^{3+} COUPLE

Acid concentration	$HClO_4$	HNO_3	H_2SO_4	HCl
1	1.70	1.61	1.44	1.28
2	1.71	1.62	1.44	
4	1.75	1.61		
6	1.82	1.56	1.43	
8	1.87		1.42	

DUKE has attempted to relate these results to recent quantitative work on the nature of ceric solutions.[28,29] Although insufficient data are available for a quantitative correlation, it is clear that the variation in the e.m.f. of the couple can be accounted for by an extensive hydrolysis and ion-association of the ceric ion.[45]

The potential of the hypothetical Pr^{4+}/Pr^{3+} couple has been estimated, from measurements of the heat of solution of the dioxide PrO_2, as 2.9 V.[46]

Direct measurements of the lanthanide reduction potentials have not been made. The evidence from polarography in aqueous solution is inconclusive, and it is believed that the observed reduction waves are caused by a catalytic evolution of hydrogen.[47]

However, in non-aqueous solvents such as acetonitrile, well defined reduction steps are observed and these are separated from the base electrolyte reduction wave. In this solvent, Sm, Eu and Yb give first a one-electron reduction, followed by a two-electron reduction. The other rare earth elements, and yttrium, give single, three-electron reduction steps.[48]

The reduction potentials of the metals have been deduced from the known values of the heats of solution of the metals, and estimated values of the entropies of the $3+$ ions.[49] These are summarised below:

TABLE 12

ESTIMATED REDUCTION POTENTIALS OF THE RARE EARTH $3+$ IONS

Element	E_{30}	Element	E_{30}	Element	E_{30}
La	2.52	Eu	2.41	Er	2.30
Ce	2.48	Gd	2.40	Tm	2.28
Pr	2.47	Tb	2.39	Yb	2.27
Nd	2.44	Dy	2.35	Lu	2.25
Sm	2.41	Ho	2.32	Y	2.37

CONCLUSIONS

The behaviour of the terpositive ions in water is entirely consistent with an increase in hydration from lanthanum to lutetium. When the terpositive ions are complexed, more individualistic behaviour is observed, and there is no simple explanation of the experimental observations. More data on entropy changes during complexing are needed. Relatively little is known of the nature of ceric solutions, and there is scope for more quantitative information. The interesting $2+$ ions are too unstable for investigation by classical methods, and their study cannot be undertaken until new techniques are developed.

REFERENCES

1 G. JONES and G. F. BICKFORD, *J. Am. Chem. Soc.*, 56 (1934) 602.
2 F. H. SPEDDING, P. E. PORTER and J. M. WRIGHT, *J. Am. Chem. Soc.*, 74 (1952) 2055.
3 F. H. SPEDDING and S. JAFFE, *J. Am. Chem. Soc.*, 76 (1954) 882.
4 F. H. SPEDDING and J. L. DYE, *J. Am. Chem. Soc.*, 76 (1954) 879.
5 I. L. JENKINS and G. B. MONK, *J. Am. Chem. Soc.*, 72 (1950) 2695.
6 F. H. SPEDDING and S. JAFFE, *J. Am. Chem. Soc.*, 76 (1954) 884.
7 C. W. DAVIES and J. C. JAMES, *Proc. Roy. Soc.*, A195 (1948) 116.
8 J. C. JAMES, *J. Chem. Soc.*, (1950) 1094.
9 N. BJERRUM, *Kgl. Danske Videnskab. Selskab*, 7 (1926) No. 9.
10 H. S. DUNSMORE and J. C. JAMES, *J. Chem. Soc.*, (1951) 2925.
11 H. S. DUNSMORE, T. R. KELLY, and G. H. NANCOLLAS, *Trans. Faraday Soc.*, 59 (1963) 2606.
12 M. H. PANCKHURST and K. G. WOOLMINGTON, *Proc. Roy. Soc.*, A244 (1958) 124.
13 G. JONES and L. T. PRENDERGAST, *J. Am. Chem. Soc.*, 58 (1936) 1476.
14 L. G. LONGSWORTH and D. A. MACINNES, *J. Am. Chem. Soc.*, 60 (1938) 3070.
15 F. H. SPEDDING, P. E. PORTER and J. M. WRIGHT, *J. Am. Chem. Soc.*, 74 (1952) 2778.
16 T. SHEDLOVSKY, *J. Am. Chem. Soc.*, 78 (1950) 3680.
17 F. H. SPEDDING, P. E. PORTER and J. M. WRIGHT, *J. Am. Chem. Soc.*, 74 (1952) 2781.
18 R. A. ROBINSON and R. H. STOKES, *Trans. Faraday Soc.*, 45 (1949) 612.
19 F. H. SPEDDING and C. F. MILLER, *J. Am. Chem. Soc.*, 74 (1952). 3158; 4195.
20 F. H. SPEDDING and J. P. FLYNN, *J. Am. Chem. Soc.*, 76 (1954) 1474; 1477.
21 F. H. SPEDDING, A. W. NAUMANN and R. E. EBERTS, *J. Am. Chem. Soc.*, 81 (1959) 23.
22 H. T. S. BRITTON, *J. Chem. Soc.*, 127 (1925) 2142.
23 T. MOELLER and H. E. KREMERS, *J. Phys. Chem.*, 48 (1944) 395.
24 T. MOELLER, *J. Phys. Chem.*, 50 (1946) 242.
25 T. MOELLER and N. FOGEL, *J. Am. Chem. Soc.*, 73 (1951) 4481.
26 G. BIEDERMANN and L. CIAVATTA, *Acta Chem. Scand.*, 15 (1961) 1347.
26a G. BIEDERMANN, L. CIAVATTA and L. NEWMAN, *Arkiv Kemi*, 22 (1964) 253; 303.
27 V. M. TARAYAN and L. A. ELIAZYAN, *Izvest. Akad. Nauk Armyan S.S.R., Ser. Khim. Nauk*, 10 (1957) 189.
28 T. J. HARDWICK and E. ROBERTSON, *Can. J. Chem.*, 29 (1951) 818.
29 T. J. HARDWICK and E. ROBERTSON, *Can. J. Chem.*, 29 (1951) 828.
30 *Stability Constants, Part 1, Organic Ligands*, The Chemical Society, London, 1957.
31 G. SCHWARZENBACH, R. GUT and G. ANDEREGG, *Helv. Chim. Acta*, 37 (1954) 937.
32 G. ANDEREGG, *Helv. Chim. Acta*, 43 (1960) 825.

33 F. H. SPEDDING, J. E. POWELL and E. J. WHEELWRIGHT, *J. Am. Chem. Soc.*, 78 (1956) 34.

34 R. HARDER and S. CHABEREK, *J. Inorg. Nucl. Chem.*, 11 (1959) 197.

35 J. L. MACKEY, M. A. HILLER and J. E. POWELL, *J. Phys. Chem.*, 66 (1962) 311.

36 R. H. BETTS and O. F. DALLINGER, *Can. J. Chem.*, 37 (1959) 91.

37 T. MOELLER and L. C. THOMPSON, *J. Inorg. Nucl. Chem.*, 24 (1962) 499.

38 A. SONESSON, *Acta Chem. Scand.*, 12 (1958) 165; 1937.

39 R. S. KOLAT and J. E. POWELL, *Inorg. Chem.*, 1 (1962) 293.

40 H. N. McCOY, *J. Am. Chem. Soc.*, 58 (1936) 1577.

41 L. B. ANDERSON and D. J. MACERO, *J. Phys. Chem.*, 67 (1963) 1942.

42 H. A. LAITINEN and W. A. TAEBEL, *Ind. Eng. Chem. (Anal. Ed.)*, 13 (1941) 825.

43 A. TIMNICK and G. GLOCKLER, *J. Am. Chem. Soc.*, 70 (1948) 1347.

44 G. F. SMITH and C. A. GETZ, *Ind. Eng. Chem. (Anal. Ed.)*, 10 (1938) 191.

45 E. WADSWORTH, F. R. DUKE and C. A. GETZ, *Anal. Chem.*, 29 (1957) 1824.

46 L. EYRING, H. LOHR and B. B. CUNNINGHAM, *J. Am. Chem. Soc.*, 74 (1952) 1186.

47 S. MISUMI and Y. IDE, *Bull. Chem. Soc. Japan*, 33 (1960) 836.

48 I. M. KOLTHOFF and J. F. COETZEE, *J. Am. Chem. Soc.*, 79 (1957) 1852.

49 W. E. LATIMER, *Oxidation Potentials*, Prentice-Hall, New York, 1952.

CHAPTER 6

Unusual valency states of the lanthanide elements

The lanthanide elements are usually terpositive in aqueous solution and in the solid state. Exceptions to this have been known for many years. For example, cerium forms the stable quadripositive oxide, and the ceric ion is well known; praseodymium and terbium also form higher oxides. Interest in the problem of unusual valency states has been stimulated by the fact that the actinide elements commonly exhibit several valency states; comparison with the behaviour of the rare earth elements is therefore of considerable theoretical interest. Observations made during work on the metallurgy of the rare-earth elements have also contributed to the isolation of new compounds with low charge numbers.

Since the ceric state is well known, it is discussed elsewhere (p. 47).

LOW VALENCY STATES

Lanthanum, cerium, praseodymium, neodymium. Certain of the rare-earth metals are known to dissolve in their molten trihalides. Electrical conductivity measurements have been made on the lanthanum–neodymium systems; molten chlorides and iodides were used.[1,2] When lanthanum or cerium metal was added to the appropriate trichloride melt, there was a progressive increase in electrical conductivity as more metal was added, to a value between four and five times that of the fused chloride. Similar additions of praseodymium metal trebled the conductivity, and the addition of neodymium increased the conductivity by 50 %. The metal–triiodide systems showed similar behaviour. These metals are soluble in the fused halides to the extent of 10–20 % moles.

References p. 69

Phase rule studies of these metal–metal-halide systems have led to the isolation of dihalides of the metals. Equilibrium is complicated if oxygen-containing impurities are present. The trihalides have therefore been prepared by the direct combination of metal and halogen, and the product was distilled before being equilibrated with metal.

The most complete study has been made of the iodide systems.[2,3,4] Highly coloured salts, of composition LnI_2, were isolated from each of these four systems. The lanthanum, cerium and praseodymium compounds had a metallic appearance and a low resistivity; the lanthanum compound was paramagnetic. The neodymium compound was an insulator and had the theoretical magnetic susceptibility for an Nd^{2+} ion; it was also isostructural with samarous dibromide. Non-stoicheiometric compounds such as $CeI_{2.4}$ and $PrI_{2.5}$ were also detected. Neodymium dichloride, $NdCl_2$, has been prepared together with two non-stoicheiometric chlorides of composition $NdCl_{2.27}$ and $NdCl_{2.37}$. Non-stoicheiometric chlorides and bromides of praseodymium are also known.[5,6,7]

The evidence in favour of bipositive neodymium appears convincing, but it is suggested that the highly conducting dihalides of La, Ce, and Pr should be formulated $(Ln^{3+}e^-)$ to account for their electronic conductivity. Further magnetic and electrical measurements are needed on these compounds.

Samarium. Bipositive samarium was first prepared by MATIGNON who reduced the trichloride with hydrogen.[8] KLEMM showed this to be a general method for the preparation of the dihalides.[9]

$$2\,SmX_3 + H_2 \rightarrow 2\,SmX_2 + 2\,HX \qquad (1)$$

Another method applicable to the diiodide was developed by JANTSCH,[10] who found that the triiodide disproportionated at a pressure of about 0.01 mm Hg.

$$2\,SmI_3 \xrightarrow{\ 700^0\ } 2\,SmI_2 + I_2 \qquad (2)$$

Reduction of the trifluorides with calcium metal, or with carbon, does not proceed further than the difluoride.[11,12]

CLIFFORD and BEACHELL prepared samarium dichloride by reducing the trichloride with magnesium in an alcoholic solution of hydrochloric acid.[13] The salt formed on the surface of the metal. The samarous ion has a purple-red colour in aqueous solution. It is a powerful reducing agent, and is rapidly oxidised by molecular oxygen, water or hydrogen ions.

Direct measurement of the potential of the Sm^{3+}/Sm^{2+} couple has not been made, but, from polarographic studies, it is known to be about 1.35 V.[14] Because of the high reactivity of Sm^{2+}, only a limited number of samarous compounds have been prepared in aqueous solution; these include the sulphate, carbonate, hydroxide and chromate. The sulphide SmS has been prepared by a solid state reaction.[15] The oxide SmO was obtained by reducing the trioxide with lanthanum metal; moreover, there is also evidence of the formation of non-stoicheiometric lower oxides.[16] (p. 91) SELWOOD has compared the magnetic susceptibility of the salts $SmBr_2$ and $EuBr_3$. Over the temperature range 80–360°K these were very similar, proving that the Sm^{2+} and Eu^{3+} ions have the same electronic configuration.[17]

Europium. Bipositive europium was prepared by URBAIN who reduced the trichloride with hydrogen.[18] This is a general method by which the dihalides of europium are prepared. There is no evidence that disproportionation of the dihalogenides occurs.

The europous ion is light yellow, and it is the divalent lanthanide ion most stable in aqueous solution, although, like the rest, it reacts with water, hydrogen ions, and molecular oxygen. A convenient preparative method was devised by McCoy, who showed that the terpositive ion was reduced quantitatively to the bipositive state in a Jones reductor.[19] McCoy made a direct measurement of the potential of the Eu^{3+}/Eu^{2+} couple and found it to be 0.43 V. This value is substantiated by the polarographic measurements by LAITINEN.[20,21] As the europous ion is relatively stable, its salts have received greater attention than those of any other bipositive lanthanides. The halides, sulphate, carbonate, and hydroxide are known, and the crystal structures of many of the compounds have been determined. Europous sulphate is isomorphous with barium sulphate, and this is exploited in isolating europium from low-grade sources.

The chalcogenides are conveniently prepared by solid state reactions.[22] Their magnetic susceptibilities have been determined. The monoxide EuO has recently been isolated by reduction of the trioxide with lanthanum metal.[16] But the trioxide is not reduced by hydrogen, although BRAUER has obtained a partial reduction by supporting the europia in a strontium oxide matrix[23] (p. 92).

SELWOOD compared the magnetic susceptibilities of Eu^{2+} and Gd^{3+} compounds; these proved to be very similar over a temperature range of 200°, showing that the two ions are isoelectronic.[17]

Thulium. The diiodide has recently been prepared by two methods involving the reduction of the triiodide with thulium metal or with mercuric iodide.[24] The dark coloured salt was isolated and shown to be isostructural with YbI_2. Bipositive thulium appears to be less stable in water than the samarous ion, and momentarily gives a violet-red colour before being oxidised by water to the terpositive ion. Magnetic measurements on this compound have not been reported.

Ytterbium. Ytterbous chloride was made by KLEMM who reduced the trichloride with hydrogen.[25] Similar methods were used by JANTSCH who prepared the dibromide and diiodide. Some evidence was found of disproportionation of the diiodide.[26]

$$3YbI_2 \rightarrow Yb + 2YbI_3 \tag{3}$$

The ytterbous ion has a bright orange colour in aqueous solution. Its reactivity is intermediate between that of Sm^{2+} and Eu^{2+}; it is readily oxidised by water, hydrogen ions, and oxygen. Direct measurement of the potential of the Yb^{3+}/Yb^{2+} couple has given unreliable results; from polarographic measurements it is known to be about 1.15 V.[21] The Yb^{2+} ion is moderately stable in cold, neutral solution, and the sulphate, carbonate, and hydroxide have been isolated. The chalcogenides, like the halides, are conveniently prepared by gas–solid reactions between the elements.[27] The oxide YbO has been prepared by reducing the sesquioxide with carbon.[27] Few magnetic measurements have been made on ytterbous salts. The susceptibilities of $YbSO_4$ and $YbCl_2$ were very much smaller than those of the terpositive salts; indeed they had only 5% of the value, but it was not certain whether the residual magnetism arose from incomplete reduction or impurity in the ytterbium source.[25,29]

HIGH VALENCY STATES

Praseodymium. Higher oxides of praseodymium have been known for many years. When ignited in air, its oxide has the composition Pr_6O_{11}.[30] PRANDTL and REIDER have suggested that praseodymium with a 5+ charge is formed in some mixed oxide systems[31] but this is known to be incorrect. Recent work by EYRING has shown that the equilibrium oxygen content of the oxide depends on temperature and oxygen pressure. The oxide PrO_2 was isolated by quenching material heated at 500° and 100 atm oxygen pressure; it had the fluorite structure.[32,33] In earlier work, oxides of composition $PrO_{1.9}$ to $PrO_{1.95}$ were obtained by treating Pr_2O_3 or Pr_6O_{11} at room temperature with ozone.[34]

Further examples of praseodymium(IV) compounds have been found among the mixed alkali metal–praseodymium salts. Attempts to prepare PrF_4 by fluorination of the trifluoride were not successful.[35] Salts of the composition M_2PrF_6 have been prepared by HOPPE, where M is an akali metal Rb, Cs, K, or Na,[36] and the structure was confirmed by a variety of physical techniques. The sodium salt has also been prepared by ASPREY.[37] However, the ion Pr^{4+} is unknown in aqueous solution. The potential of the couple Pr^{4+}/Pr^{3+} has been estimated to be 2.9 V from measurements of the heat of solution of the oxide PrO_2.[38]

Neodymium, dysprosium. Attempts to prepare neodymium (IV) and dysprosium (IV) compounds by direct fluorination were not successful. However, methods similar to those used for making praseodymium (IV) compounds were more encouraging. When mixtures of neodymium or dysprosium salts with either rubidium or caesium halides were fluorinated, the absorption spectrum of the original 3+ ions was replaced by a new spectrum, and the products had a face-centred cubic structure. The analytical evidence suggests that half of the lanthanide ions present were quadripositive.[38]

Terbium. Non-stoicheiometric higher oxides of terbium have been recognised for many years. The material obtained by heating the oxide in air at 800° has a composition approximating to Tb_4O_7. The dioxide, TbO_2, was first isolated by KATZ, who used atomic oxygen as the oxidising agent.[40] Systematic work by EYRING has shown that the composition of the oxide depends on oxygen pressure and temperature.[33,41] The isotherms were more complex than those obtained with the praseodymium oxides and there was some hysteresis. The oxide TbO_2 has the fluorite structure.

The tetrafluoride TbF_4 has been prepared by fluorination of the trifluoride at 300–400°. It is isostructural with CeF_4.[42]

The ion Tb^{4+} is not known in solution. Presumably it is a powerful oxidising agent, since TbO_2 dissolves in hydrochloric acid with the evolution of chlorine. The potential of the couple Tb^{4+}/Tb^{3+} is unknown but is probably about the same as that of the Pr^{4+}/Pr^{3+} couple.

EFFECT OF CHARGE ON IONIC SIZE

The sizes of some of the Ln^{2+} and Ln^{4+} ions have been determined.

TABLE 13

VARIATION OF IONIC SIZE WITH CHARGE NUMBER

Element	Ln^{4+}	Ln^{3+}	Ln^{2+}
Ce	0.92	1.03	
Pr	0.90	1.01	
Sm		0.96	1.11
Eu		0.95	1.09
Tb	0.84	0.92	
Tm		0.87	0.94
Yb		0.86	0.93

In Table 13 they are compared with the data of TEMPLETON on the tervalent ions.[43]

CONCLUSIONS

It is now thought that ten of the lanthanide elements exhibit valency states other than three; in some cases, confirmatory magnetic evidence has yet to be obtained. The present position is summarised in Table 14.

TABLE 14

VALENCY STATES OF THE LANTHANIDE ELEMENTS

Element	Atomic number	4f electrons	Solution	Solid state
La	57	0	3	2(?) 3
Ce	58	2	3,4	2(?) 3,4
Pr	59	3	3	2(?) 3,4
Nd	60	4	3	2,3,4(?)
Sm	62	6	2,3	2,3
Eu	63	7	2,3	2,3
Tb	65	9	3	3,4
Dy	66	10	3	3,4 (?)
Tm	69	13	3	2(?) 3
Yb	70	14	2,3	2,3

REFERENCES

1 H. R. BRONSTEIN, A. S. DWORKIN and M. A. BREDIG, *J. Phys. Chem.*, 66 (1962) 44.
2 A. S. DWORKIN, R. A. SALLACH, H. R. BRONSTEIN, M. A. BREDIG and J. D. CORBETT, *J. Phys. Chem.*, 67 (1963) 1145.
3 J. D. CORBETT, L. F. DRUDING and C. B. LINDAHL, *J. Inorg. Nucl. Chem.*, 17 (1961) 176.
4 J. D. CORBETT, L. F. DRUDING, W. J. BURKHARD and C. B. LINDAHL, *Discussions Faraday Soc.*, 32 (1961) 79.
5 J. F. DRUDING and J. D. CORBETT, *J. Am. Chem. Soc.*, 83 (1961) 2462.
6 R. A. SALLACH and J. D. CORBETT, *Inorg. Chem.*, 2 (1963) 457; 3 (1964) 933.

7 L. F. DRUDING, J. D. CORBETT and B. N. RAMSEY, *Inorg. Chem.*, 2 (1963) 869.
8 C. MATIGNON and E. CAZES, *Compt. Rend.*, 142 (1906) 83.
9 W. KLEMM and J. ROCKSTROH, *Z. Anorg. Allgem. Chem.*, 176 (1928) 181.
10 G. JANTSCH and N. SKALLA, *Z. Anorg. Allgem. Chem.*, 193 (1930) 391.
11 F. H. SPEDDING and A. H. DAANE, *J. Am. Chem. Soc.*, 74 (1952) 2783.
12 A. R. KIRCHENBAUM and J. CAHILL, *J. Inorg. Nucl. Chem.*, 14 (1960) 148.
13 A. F. CLIFFORD and H. C. BEACHELL, *J. Am. Chem. Soc.*, 70 (1948) 2730.
14 A. TIMNICK and G. GLOCKLER, *J. Am. Chem. Soc.*, 70 (1948) 1347.
15 M. PICON and M. PATRIE, *Compt. Rend.*, 242 (1956) 1321.
16 H. A. EICK, N. C. BAENZIGER and L. EYRING, *J. Am. Chem. Soc.*, 78 (1956) 5147.
17 P. W. SELWOOD, *J. Am. Chem. Soc.*, 55 (1933) 4869.
18 G. URBAIN and F. BOURION, *Compt. Rend.*, 153 (1911) 1155.
19 H. N. McCOY, *J. Am. Chem. Soc.*, 57 (1935) 1756.
20 H. N. McCOY, *J. Am. Chem. Soc.*, 58 (1936) 1577.
21 H. A. LAITINEN and W. A. TAEBEL, *Ind. Eng. Chem. (Anal. Edn.)*, 13 (1941) 825.
22 W. KLEMM and H. SENFF, *Z. Anorg. Allgem. Chem.*, 241 (1939) 259.
23 G. BRAUER, R. MULLER and K. H. ZAPP, *Z. Anorg. Allgem. Chem.*, 280 (1955) 40.
24 L. B. ASPREY and F. H. KRUSE, *J. Inorg. Nucl. Chem.*, 13 (1960) 32.
25 W. KLEMM and W. SCHUTT, *Z. Anorg. Allgem. Chem.*, 184 (1929) 352.
26 G. JANTSCH, N. SKALLA and H. JAWUREK, *Z. Anorg. Allgem. Chem.*, 201 (1931) 207.
27 H. SENFF and W. KLEMM, *Z. Anorg. Allgem. Chem.*, 242 (1939) 92.
28 J. C. ACKLAND and G. TSOUCONS, *Compt. Rend.*, 246 (1958) 285.
29 G. HUGHES and D. W. PEARCE, *J. Am. Chem. Soc.*, 55 (1933) 3277.
30 P. H. M. BRINTON and H. A. PAGEL, *J. Am. Chem. Soc.*, 45 (1923) 1460.
31 W. PRANDTL and G. REIDER, *Z. Anorg. Allgem. Chem.*, 238 (1938) 225.
32 R. E. FERGUSON, E. D. GUTH and L. EYRING, *J. Am. Chem. Soc.*, 76 (1954) 3890.
33 W. SIMON and L. EYRING, *J. Am. Chem. Soc.*, 76 (1954) 5872.
34 S. RABIDEAU and G. GLOCKLER, *J. Am. Chem. Soc.*, 73 (1951) 488.
35 T. F. PERROS and C. R. NAESER, *J. Am. Chem. Soc.*, 74 (1952) 3694.
36 R. HOPPE, *Angew. Chem.*, 71 (1959) 457.
37 L. B. ASPREY and T. R. KEENAN, *J. Inorg. Nucl. Chem.*, 16 (1961) 260.
38 L. EYRING, H. LOHR and B. B. CUNNINGHAM, *J. Am. Chem. Soc.*, 74 (1952) 1186.
39 L. B. ASPREY, *Rare Earth Research*, Ed. E. V. KLEBER, McMillan, New York, 1961.
40 D. M. GRUEN, W. [C. KOCHLER and J. J. KATZ, *J. Am. Chem. Soc.*, 73 (1951) 1475.
41 E. D. GUTH and L. EYRING, *J. Am. Chem. Soc.*, 76 (1954) 5242.
42 B. B. CUNNINGHAM, D. C. FEAY and M. A. ROLLIER, *J. Am. Chem. Soc.*, 76 (1954) 3361.
43 D. H. TEMPLETON and C. H. DAUBEN, *J. Am. Chem. Soc.*, 76 (1954) 5237.

CHAPTER 7

Compounds with elements from Groups I, III, IV, and V

The rare earth elements form compounds with a number of the elements from these groups of the Periodic Table. Their preparation and properties are discussed.

HYDRIDES AND DEUTERIDES

Hydrides of the lanthanide elements were discovered in 1891; they are prepared by direct combination of the elements.[1,2] As rare-earth metals of high purity have only recently become available, emphasis is placed on the more recent investigations; this has undoubtedly confirmed some of the earlier work on light earth systems.[3]

The formation of hydrides has been studied by introducing the carefully cleaned metal into a high vacuum system, and, after out-gassing, heating it to the reaction temperature and allowing it to equilibriate with purified hydrogen or deuterium. The composition of the solid is controlled by the temperature and equilibrium pressure. Before physical examination, the hydride samples are annealed for some hours at a lower temperature.[3]

Hydrogen pressure–composition isotherms have been obtained for yttrium and many of the lanthanide elements.[3,4,5,6,7] Isotherms for the hydrogen–praseodymium system are shown in Fig. 9.

During the reaction, the metal rapidly picks up hydrogen at low pressures, and this is followed by a constant-pressure plateau in which the dihydride composition LnH_2 is approached. An increase in gas pressure is required to attain the dihydride composition

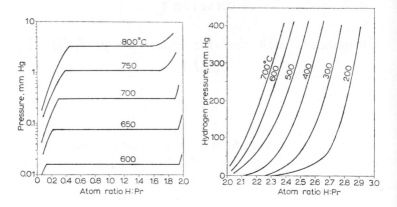

Fig. 9. Pressure–composition isotherms for the praseodymium–hydrogen system. [Reproduced, with permission, from *J. Phys. Chem.*, 59 (1955) 1222.]

and further substantial pressure increases result in the limiting trihydride composition being approached.

X-ray examination shows that hydrogen first dissolves in the metal and then, as the hydrogen present increases beyond $LnH_{0.1}$, the dihydride phase appears, and two phases are present until the overall composition approaches LnH_2. The dihydrides have the fluorite structure.[8] As the light earth hydrides approach the LnH_3 composition, the dihydride phase only is present, and neutron diffraction shows the additional hydrogen to be distributed randomly through the lattice. But the heavy earth hydrides undergo a structural change when the proportion of hydrogen exceeds that for the dihydride, and a hexagonal phase appears. There is a range of overall composition in which both fluorite and hexagonal forms are present and finally only the hexagonal structure remains. The hydrides form two isostructural series which are not influenced by the crystal structure of the metals.

The hydrides are all less dense than the metals. However, a lattice contraction is observed on passing from the dihydride to the trihydride composition with all lanthanides. When plotted against atomic number, the lattice parameters of the cubic dihydrides and the hexagonal trihydrides both decrease.[3]

Exceptions to this behaviour are found with europium and ytterbium, since under comparable reaction conditions only the dihydrides are formed.[9] Their dihydrides and dideuterides are orthorhombic and are isomorphous with the alkaline earth hydrides. A higher hydride of ytterbium, $YbH_{2.5}$, has been prepared in hydrogen at 60 atm pressure. Magnetic measurements on this material suggested that some YbH_3 was present. A corresponding experiment with europium gave EuH_2 only.[10]

Properties of hydrides

It is thought that the hydrides are salt-like, the hydrogen being present as an anion and acquiring its electron from the conduction band of the metal. This is in agreement with the stoicheiometry of the hydrides; europium and ytterbium, which are bipositive in the metallic state, normally form dihydrides.* Magnetic measurements on hydrides of differing compositions show that the charge number is unchanged by hydrogenation.[11, 12, 13, 14] The resistivity of the metal is substantially unchanged by hydrogenation until the dihydride composition is approached, but a very large increase (from 10^5 to 10^6) is found between the di- and the tri-hydride compositions. Moreover, the resistivity has a low temperature coefficient at dihydride composition, but the temperature coefficient is negative when the trihydride composition is reached.[12] The contraction observed on passing from the dihydride to the trihydride is due to the removal of electrons from the conduction band; these screen the lanthanide and hydride ions, and, as they are removed there is an increased attraction between the oppositely charged ions.[3]

The hydrides are brittle solids, which dissociate on heating. At room temperature, the dihydrides are stable in air but some of the trihydrides are pyrophoric. All the hydrides are slowly attacked by water, and rapidly by acids.

---

* The generally accepted picture of metals is that the cations are in fixed positions in the crystal lattice, surrounded by an electron cloud. Unlike those of covalent structures, these electrons are delocalized; many of the characteristic properties of the metallic state are thus explained.

References p. 82

BORIDES

Two types of boride, the tetraboride LnB_4 and hexaboride LnB_6, are known for all of the lanthanides. Complete phase rule studies of boron, with lanthanum and yttrium, have been made by metallographic and X-ray techniques, and additional compounds were disclosed in these investigations.[15,16]

Methods of preparation

1. Electrolysis of lanthanide oxide in a fused borate bath. Alkali and alkaline earth fluorides are added to the bath to reduce the melting point and viscosity. Electrolysis is carried out in a graphite crucible at 950–1000°, at 3–15 V. The crucible forms the anode, and water-cooled carbon or molybdenum cathodes are used. The product contains more boron than is required for the hexaboride, owing to the formation of boron itself at the cathode. The yield of boride is low.[17,18]

2. Reduction of rare earth and boron oxides with carbon. Boric oxide is volatile at the reaction temperature, and the products are contaminated with a little carbon.[19]

$$Ln_2O_3 + 4 B_2O_3 + 15 C \rightarrow 2 LnB_4 + 15 CO$$

3. Reduction of lanthanide oxides with boron carbide. Depending on the boride required, additional boron or carbon is added and the mixtures are pelleted, and fired at 1500–1800° in a vacuum or in hydrogen. The products have a low carbon content.[20,21,22]

$$Ln_2O_3 + 3 B_4C \rightarrow 2 LnB_6 + 3 CO$$

4. Reduction of the lanthanide oxides with boron. Reaction is carried out at 1500–1800° in zirconium boride or molybdenum containers; boron monoxide sublimes during the process. A range of borides has been prepared by this method.[20,23]

$$Ln_2O_3 + 11 B \rightarrow 2 LnB_4 + 3 BO \uparrow$$

5. Direct combination of the elements.

The reactants are pelleted and fired in a vacuum or in argon at 1300–2000°. The cerium and lanthanum compounds have been prepared in this way.[16,24]

Structure of the borides

LnB_2. The yttrium compound YB_2 has a hexagonal structure.[18,25]

LnB_3. This phase has been found for a number of the borides of several rare earths and yttrium.[20,25] The structure is stated to be tetragonal, but this was not found to be so by LUNDIN.[16]

LnB_4. These compounds are known for yttrium and all the lanthanides except europium.[18,19,21] The structure is hexagonal, and the lattice parameters decrease with atomic number; the compounds have ionic bonding.

LnB_6. These compounds are known for yttrium and the lanthanides from La to Ho, but attempts to prepare the hexaborides of Er, Tm, and Lu were unsuccessful.[26] The structure is of the cubic CsCl-type; metal atoms occupy the corners of the cube with boron octahedra at the body centre of each unit cell. The lattice dimensions follow the atomic radius of the rare earth metals, the dimensions for europium and ytterbium being anomalous. This suggests a metallic type of bonding, which is confirmed by the high electrical conductivity.[20,21,23]

LnB_{12}. The yttrium compound has been made, also the Dy to Lu compounds, but attempts to prepare dodecaborides of the lighter elements failed.[27] They have a rigid boron network, with the metal in cubo-octahedral holes.

Physical properties

Magnetic measurements on the hexaborides show that the lanthanide ions are terpositive. Their resistivity, of the same magnitude as the lanthanide metals, proves a metallic type of bonding.[18,] The hexaborides have low work functions and high thermionic emission currents*; these properties have been measured for a number of hexaborides.[21,29] SAMSONOV has suggested that the high thermionic emission is caused by a donor-acceptor mechanism between metal and boron atoms.[21]

Chemical properties

The most stable compounds are the hexaborides; when other borides are heated in a vacuum, they tend to the hexaboride composition. The lower borides are hydrolysed by water or acids with evolution of boron hydrides, but the hexaborides are unaffected by this treatment. The latter are decomposed when heated with sulphuric or nitric acid, or when fused with alkalis or alkaline bisulphates.[28] They are oxidised in air above 1000°. This exceptional stability is attributed to the octahedral arrangement of the boron atoms.

CARBIDES

The carbides have been known since 1896, but they have been studied systematically only during the last ten years.[30,31] Three main types of carbide are known, Ln_3C, Ln_2C_3, and LnC_2, although several other types have been prepared. A phase diagram for the lanthanum–carbon system has been drawn.[32]

Methods of preparation

1. Lanthanide oxide and carbon are heated together above 2000° in a graphite crucible under argon.[30,31,33,36] When a small excess of carbon is present the dicarbide is formed.

---

* The work function is the energy required to remove an electron from the Fermi level to infinity. The Fermi level divides unoccupied levels from those occupied by electrons. Work function and thermionic emission are related by the equation

$$I = AT^2 e^{-\phi/kT}$$

where ϕ is the work function, I the current density in A/cm^2, A the emission current density constant, T the temperature (°K), and k is Boltzmann's constant.

$$Ln_2O_3 + 7\ C \rightarrow 2\ LnC_2 + 3\ CO$$

2. Metal filings and the required quantity of carbon are mixed and pelletted, and either arc melted or heated in a tantalum crucible.[32,34,35,37]

3. The metal hydride and graphite are mixed and heated at 1000° in a vacuum.[39]

Structure of the carbides

Ln_3C. Of this type, the yttrium and Sm–Lu compounds are known.[32] The structure is face-centred cubic, Fe_4N type, with four metal atoms per unit cell. There is evidence that the non-stoicheiometry varies between $YC_{0.25}$ and $YC_{0.4}$ for the yttrium compound. The structural parameters of the ytterbium compound are anomalous. It is possible that the ion may be bipositive in this compound, but magnetic measurements have not been reported.

LnC. Only the cerium compound has been reported among the lanthanides, although scandium monocarbide is known.[41] The latter may be a solid solution of carbon in the metal.

Ln_2C_3. The yttrium and La–Ho compounds are known. They have a body-centred structure of the Pu_2C_3 type.[41] Some variation in their lattice parameters suggests the possibility of variable stoicheiometry. The carbon–carbon bond length is olefinic.[38]

LnC_2. This form is known for yttrium and all the lanthanide elements. The structure is body-centre tetragonal of the CaC_2 type, with two molecules per unit cell. The carbon–carbon bond length is intermediate between the olefinic and acetylinic.[38] The YbC_2 compound has abnormal structural parameters.[32]

Properties of the carbides.

The sesquicarbides and dicarbides both display metallic conductivity.[37,43] Magnetic measurements on the dicarbides show the lanthanide ions to be terpositive except in the samarium and ytterbium compounds, where some bipositive ions are present. Melting points of the dicarbides are above 2000°.

All the carbides are hydrolysed in water at room temperature, giving the lanthanide hydroxide and gaseous products. The Ln_3C carbides give a mixture of methane and hydrogen. The sesquicarbides and dicarbides react to give acetylene (50% and 70% respectively) together with hydrogen and small quantities of C_2 and C_3 hydrocarbons. Ytterbium dicarbide, in which the metal is bipositive, gives mainly acetylene and no hydrogen.

These results suggest that the nature of the gaseous products is mainly controlled by the carbon–carbon distances in the carbides; the water molecules acquire electrons from the conduction band of the carbide and produce nascent hydrogen. The reaction of ytterbium dicarbide resembles that of the alkaline earth carbides.[32,44]

The reaction of carbides with acids is more difficult to interpret, owing to the reduction of the anion and the formation of carbon.[39]

SILICIDES

The rare-earth silicides have been little studied. Two types of compound have been identified, Ln_3Si_5 for the middle and heavy earths, and the disilicide, $LnSi_2$, for the light and middle earths. A recent examination of the yttrium–silicon system gave evidence of four yttrium-silicon compounds.[45]

Methods of preparation
1. Electrolysis of lanthanide oxides in a fused silicate bath, in which the electrolyte is a ternary mixture of calcium silicate, calcium fluoride, and calcium chloride. When electrolysed at 1000^0 at 8–10 V, silicides are formed on the cathode as metallic-like granules. The boule is removed and crushed, and when extracted with caustic soda to remove silica, leaves a residue with some excess of silicon.[46]
2. Reduction of a lanthanide oxide with silicon. The reactants are powdered, mixed, and heated in a corundum boat in a vacuum at 1100–1600°. Light and middle disilicides have been prepared in this way, although the composition of the gadolinium compound was $GdSi_{1.47}$.[47,48]

$$Ln_2O_3 + 7\,Si \rightarrow 2\,LnSi_2 + 3\,SiO \uparrow$$

3. Direct union of the elements. Silicon and metal are pelletted, and arc-melted in a vacuum. Lanthanum disilicide has been prepared thus, but attempts with cerium gave products containing several silicides.[48,49]

Structure of the silicides

The phase-rule study of the Y–Si system gave evidence for Y_5Si_3, Y_5Si_4, YSi and Y_3Si_5, but none for a disilicide YSi_2.[45]

LnSi. Only the yttrium compound has been examined. A preparation obtained by arc-melting was orthorhombic of the CaSi type.[50]

$LnSi_2$. Recent work has shown the light and middle earth disilicides to have two structures; the transition temperatures vary with atomic number.[49,51] The low temperature form is orthorhombic; the high temperature form is tetragonal and has the $ThSi_2$ structure.[47] Disilicides of the heavier earths (Er to Ln) are hexagonal and transformations have not been observed.[52,53]

Properties of the silicides

The melting points of the disilicides are between 1500° and 1550°. A number of properties of the lanthanide compounds have been measured.[54] The resistivity is greater than that of the metals. The temperature coefficient of resistivity is positive, but changes sign at 500°; it is not known whether this is due to a change in conduction mechanism or to the polymorphic transition. The Seebeck coefficient* is negative from 100° to 1000°, but there is a minimum at 500–600°. This suggests that conduction is n-type up to 500°, and p-type above 500°.

The disilicides are attacked by aqueous HCl or HF. They are decomposed by a molten Na_2CO_3–K_2CO_3 eutectic.

---

* When two metals are connected to form a circuit, and the two junctions are kept at different temperatures, a thermoelectric potential is developed. The Seebeck coefficient is the slope of the temperature–potential curve.

References p. 82

NITRIDES

The rare earth nitrides were discovered by MATIGNON.[55]

Methods of preparation

1. Reaction of metal and nitrogen. The classical method is to pass nitrogen over the metal heated to 800–1000°. Alternatively a closed system may be used and the progress of the reaction followed by the fall in the nitrogen pressure. The dissociation of titanium nitride is a convenient source of nitrogen for the purpose.

$$2 \, Ln + N_2 \rightarrow 2 \, LnN$$

2. Reaction of nitrogen on the metal hydride. As a first step, the metal hydride is made by direct union of the elements at 500°, and this is allowed to react with nitrogen at 900–1000°.

Alternatively, the hydride is caused to dissociate in a high vacuum, and the reactive metal, obtained without previous contact with air, is heated in nitrogen. Both methods require less time than the direct nitriding of the metal.[56,57]

Structure of the nitrides

They have the cubic NaCl structure. The lattice parameters vary with the radii of the terpositive ions in a linear manner.[58,59]

Properties of the nitrides

The nitrides are stable at high temperatures. The yttrium compound melted at 2570° on a tungsten support but at 2050° on graphite, presumably through the formation of carbides. When ytterbium nitride was heated with the metal at 1400° and 10^{-5}mm, both metal and nitride were found in the distillate. It seems probable that this nitride, like ytterbium metal, has an unusually high vapour pressure.[57,60]

Moist air slowly hydrolyses the nitrides with evolution of ammonia. They are rapidly dissolved by acids and hydrolysed by alkalis to the hydroxides with the liberation of ammonia.[61]

PHOSPHIDES, ARSENIDES, ANTIMONIDES AND BISMUTHIDES

Lanthanide compounds with phosphorus, arsenic, antimony and bismuth have received comparatively little attention. Interest has centred mainly on the crystal structures of the 1 : 1 compounds of the light earth elements.

Phosphides

The compounds may be prepared by enclosing the elements together in a sealed tube and gradually increasing the temperature to 900°. The material is periodically removed, ground, and reheated.[62,63] Alternatively, the reaction may be carried out under pressure in a hot press at 1000°.[64] The reaction vessel is quenched, and the product heated at 600° in a vacuum to remove the excess of phosphorus.

The lanthanum–samarium compounds have been prepared. They have the cubic NaCl structure.

Arsenides

The compounds are prepared by direct union in a sealed tube. Heating is continued for 10–15 h at a temperature of 1000–1050°. The lanthanum–samarium compounds are known. They have the cubic NaCl structure.[65,66]

Antimonides

Compounds (1 : 1) are prepared by direct union in a sealed tube which is heated to 1000–1050° for several hours. Those formed by the La–Sm metals have the cubic NaCl structure.[67]

A phase diagram for the La–Sb system has been constructed from thermal and metallographic results.[68] The compound La_3Sb_2 melted at 1700°, and the peritectic formation of La_2Sb, LaSb and $LaSb_2$ was observed.

References p. 82

Bismuthides

Compounds (1 : 1) are prepared by direct union in a sealed tube. The La–Sm compounds have the cubic NaCl structure.[69, 70, 72] There is already a phase diagram for the Ce–Bi system. Ce_4Bi_3 which melted at 1630°, and three other phases, namely Ce_3Bi, CeBi, and $CeBi_2$, were detected.[71]

Few physical data are available on the Group V compounds of the rare earths. The resistivity and Seebeck co-efficients of some arsenides and bismuthides have been determined; the materials have semiconducting properties (p. 148). The phosphides, arsenides and antimonides are slowly hydrolysed in moist air with the evolution of volatile hydrides.

REFERENCES

Hydrides and Deuterides

1 WINKLER, *Ber.*, 24 (1891) 873, 1966.
2 C. MATIGNON, *Compt. Rend.*, 131 (1900) 891.
3 A. PEBLER and W. E. WALLACE, *J. Phys. Chem.*, 66 (1962) 148.
4 R. N. R. MULFORD and C. E. HOLLEY, *J. Phys. Chem.*, 59 (1955) 1222.
5 G. E. STURDY and R. N. R. MULFORD, *J. Am. Chem. Soc.*, 78 (1956) 1083.
6 R. STRECK and K. DIALER, *Z. Anorg. Allgem. Chem.*, 306 (1960) 141.
7 C. F. LUDIN and J. P. BLACKLEDGE, *J. Electrochem. Soc.*, 109 (1962) 838.
8 C. E. HOLLEY, R. N. R. MULFORD, E. F. ELLINGER, W. C. KOEHLER and W. H. ZACHARIASEN, *J. Phys. Chem.*, 59 (1955) 1226.
9 W. L. KORST and J. C. WARF, *Acta Cryst.*, 9 (1956) 452.
10 J. C. WARF and K. HARDCASTLE, *J. Am. Chem. Soc.*, 83 (1961) 2206.
11 F. TROMBE, *Compt. Rend.*, 219 (1944) 182.
12 B. STALINSKI, *Bull. Acad. Polon. Sci.*, III (1957) 997, 1001.
13 J. N. DAOU, *Compt. Rend.*, 247 (1958) 1595.
14 Y. KUBOTA and W. E. WALLACE, *J. Chem. Phys.*, 39 (1963) 1285.

Borides

15 R. W. JOHNSON and A. H. DAANE, *J. Phys. Chem.*, 65 (1961) 909.
16 C. LUNDIN and D. KLODT, University of Denver, unpublished report.
17 L. ANDRIEUX, *Compt. Rend.*, 186 (1928) 1736; 194 (1932) 720.
18 M. VON STACKELBERG and F. NEWMAN, *Z. Phys. Chem.*, B19 (1932) 314.
19 H. BLUMENTHAL, *Powder Met. Bull.*, 7 (1956) 79.
20 B. POST, D. MOSKOWITZ and F. W. GLASER, *J. Am. Chem. Soc.*, 78 (1956) 1800.

21 G. Samsanov, *Usp. Khim.*, 28 (1959) 189.
22 N. M. Tvorogov, *Russ. J. Inorg. Chem.*, 4 (1959) 890.
23 H. A. Eick and P. W. Gillies, *J. Am. Chem. Soc.*, 81 (1959) 5030.
24 L. Brewer, D. L. Sawyer, D. H. Templeton and C. H. Dauben. *J. Am. Ceram. Soc.*, 34 (1957) 173.
25 I. Binder, *Powder Met. Bull.*, 7 (1956) 74.
26 G. D. Sturgeon and H. A. Eick, *Inorganic Chem.*, 2 (1963) 430.
27 S. LaPlace, I. Binder and B. Post, *J. Inorg. Nucl. Chem.*, 18 (1961) 113.
28 L. Andrieux, *Ann. Chim.*, 12 (1929) 423.
29 J. M. Lafferty, *J. Appl. Phys.*, 22 (1951) 299.

Carbides

30 H. Moissan, *Compt. Rend.*, 122 (1896) 148; 131 (1900) 595; 924.
31 A. Damiens, *Ann. Chim.*, 10 (1910) 137; 330.
32 F. H. Spedding, K. Gschneider and A. H. Daane, *J. Am. Chem. Soc.*, 80 (1958) 4499.
33 F. Fickter and C. Scholly, *Helv. Chem. Acta*, 3 (1920) 164.
34 M. Stackleburg, *Z. Phys. Chem.*, 139 (1930) 437.
35 F. Trombe, *Compt. Rend.*, 219 (1944) 182.
36 R. C. Vickery, R. Sedlacek and A. Reuben, *J. Chem. Soc.*, (1959) 498.
37 F. H. Spedding, K. Gschneider and A. H. Daane, *Trans. Met. Soc. A.I.M.E.*, 215 (1959) 192.
38 M. Atoji, K. Gschneider, A. H. Daane, R. E. Rundle and F. H. Spedding, *J. Am. Chem. Soc.*, 80 (1958) 1804.
39 N. N. Greenwood and A. J. Osborn, *J. Chem. Soc.*, (1961) 1775.
40 O. Krikorian, A.E.C. Publication, *U.C.R.L.*, (1955), 2888, 30-31.
41 W. H. Zachariasen, *Acta Cryst.*, 5 (1952) 17.
42 J. C. Warf, unpublished report.
43 R. C. Vickery, R. Sedlacek and A. Reuben, *J. Chem. Soc.*, (1959) 503; 505.
44 G. J. Palenick and J. C. Warf, *Inorg. Chem.*, 1 (1962) 345.

Silicides

45 C. Lundin and D. Klodt, University of Denver, unpublished report.
46 M. Dodero, *Bull. Soc. Chim.*, (1950) 545.
47 G. Brauer and H. Haag, *Z. Anorg. Allgem. Chem.*, 267 (1952) 198.
48 J. A. Perri, I. Binder and B. Post, *J. Phys. Chem.*, 63 (1959) 616.
49 L. Brewer and O. Krikorian, *J. Electrochem. Soc.*, 103 (1956) 38.
50 E. Parthé, *Acta Cryst.*, 13 (1960) 878.
51 J. Perri, E. Banks and B. Post, *J. Phys. Chem.*, 63 (1959) 2073.
52 I. P. Meyer, E. Banks and B. Post, *J. Phys. Chem.*, 66 (1962) 693.
53 A. G. Tharp, *J. Phys. Chem.*, 66 (1962) 758.
54 G. V. Samsonov, *Usp. Khim.*, 31 (1962) 1478.

Nitrides

55 C. Matignon, *Compt. Rend.*, 131 (1900) 837.

56 H. A. EICK, N. C. BAENZINGER and L. EYRING, *J. Am. Chem. Soc.*, 78 (1956) 5987.
57 C. P. KEMPSTER, N. H. KRIKORIAN and J. C. MCGUIRE, *J. Phys. Chem.*, 61 (1957) 1237.
58 W. KLEMM and G. WINKELMANN, *Z. Anorg. Allgem. Chem.*, 288 (1956) 87.
59 A. IANDELLI and E. BOTTI, *Atti Accad. Lincei*, 25 (1937) 129 ; 638.
60 R. A. YOUNG and W. T. ZEIGLER, *J. Am. Chem. Soc.*, 74 (1952) 5251.
61 M. D. LYNTAYA and C. V. SAMSONOV, *Ukr. Khim. Zh.*, 29 (1963) 251.

Phosphides

62 A. IANDELLI and E. BOTTI, *Atti Accad. Lincei*, 24 (1936) 459.
63 A. IANDELLI and E. BOTTI, *Atti Accad. Lincei*, 25 (1937) 638.
64 D. F. LA VALLE, *J. Inorg. Nucl. Chem.*, 24 (1962) 930.

Arsenides

65 A. IANDELLI and E. BOTTI, *Atti Accad. Lincei*, 25 (1937) 498.
66 A. IANDELLI, *Z. Anorg. Allgem. Chem.*, 288 (1956) 81.

Antimonides

67 A. IANDELLI and E. BOTTI, *Atti Accad. Lincei*, 25 (1937) 638.
68 R. VOGEL and H. KLOSE, *Z. Metallk.*, 48 (1954) 633.

Bismuthides

69 A. IANDELLI, *Z. Anorg. Allgem. Chem.*, 288 (1956) 81.
70 A. IANDELLI and E. BOTTI, *Atti Accad. Lincei*, 25 (1937) 233.
71 R. VOGEL, *Z. Anorg. Allgem. Chem.*, 84 (1914) 327.
72 L. H. BRIXNER, *J. Inorg. Nucl. Chem.*, 15 (1960) 199.

CHAPTER 8

Rare earth oxides

The rare earth oxides are usually prepared by pyrolysing an insoluble lanthanide salt, the oxalate or carbonate being employed. The nitrates and sulphates also pyrolyse to the oxide but require higher temperatures, and the halides are converted quantitatively to the oxide only under pyrohydrolytic conditions, that is in super-heated steam.

When prepared thermally, sesquioxides of the stoicheiometric composition Ln_2O_3 are obtained in all but three cases. The stable oxide of cerium is the dioxide CeO_2, and praseodymium and terbium form non-stoicheiometric oxides described conventionally as Pr_6O_{11} and Tb_4O_7 respectively. Recently, some lower oxides of samarium, europium and ytterbium have been prepared and characterised.

STRUCTURE OF THE OXIDES

The rare earth oxides possess one of four structural forms. Ceric oxide, and the dioxides of praseodymium and terbium, have the fluorite structure. The sesquioxides fall into one or more of the three structures A, B and C, depending on the size of the cation and the thermal history of the material. The non-stoicheiometric oxides of cerium, praseodymium and terbium form a range of defect structures depending on the equilibrium oxygen pressure and the thermal history of the specimen.

The structure of the oxides was first examined by GOLDSCHMIDT in a classical investigation.[1] He assigned the fluorite structure to ceric oxide, and this has been confirmed by all later work. For the sesquioxides, he advanced the three structures A, B and C.

In the *A* structure (Fig 10, *a*, *b*) the lanthanide ion has an unusual 7 co-ordination. Six oxygen atoms have an octahedral grouping round the metal, the additional oxygen being added above one face of the octahedron.[2,3] The metal is also 7 co-ordinate in the *B* structure; six of the oxygen atoms have an octahedral arrangement, the remaining oxygen–metal bond being unusually long.[4,5] Each metal ion in the fluorite structure is surrounded by eight oxygen atoms at the corners of a cube, while each oxygen atom is surrounded by four metal ions at the corners of a tetrahedron (Fig. 10 *d*). The *C* structure (Fig. 10 *c*) is related to the fluorite structure by removing one-quarter of the anions. The metal is 6 co-ordinate, half of the missing oxygens being on a body diagonal, alternating with a face diagonal.[6] This similarity between the fluorite

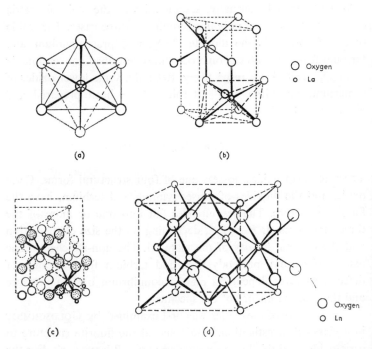

Fig. 10. Structures of the rare earth oxides. [Reproduced, with permission, from *"Structural Inorganic Chemistry"* by A. F. WELLS, Oxford University Press.]

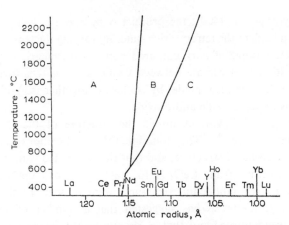

Fig. 11. Phase diagram of the rare earth sesquioxides. [Reproduced, with permission, from *J. Phys. Chem.*, 65 (1961) 2048.]

and *C* structures probably accounts for the ease with which mixed crystals are produced by the *C* type sesquioxides and the higher oxides of cerium, praseodymium and terbium.

GOLDSCHMIDT produced a phase diagram for the sesquioxides, but, as might be expected, it has been modified in detail by later work. A recent diagram by ROY, based on material obtained by hydrothermal methods, is shown in Fig. 11, and is in reasonable agreement with others in which material prepared by a quenching technique was used.[7,8]

Transformations of the sesquioxides are reversible. The present view is that the *A* form occurs only with the elements from lanthanum to praseodymium. The *C* structure alone is found for yttrium and the elements from holmium to lutetium. This structure is stable at low temperatures for the remaining elements, but the *B* structure can be obtained by quenching the *C* structure oxides from a moderate to high temperature.

NON-STOICHEIOMETRIC OXIDES

Cerium. The terpositive oxide is prepared by reducing the dioxide with hydrogen at 1400°; the product is pyrophoric, being readily oxidised back to the tetrapositive state. By varying the temperature, however, a range of dark coloured non-stoicheiometric oxides of composition intermediate between Ce_2O_3 and CeO_2 is formed.[10] Such oxides are also made by sintering together suitable proportions of sesquioxide and dioxide.

BRAUER and BEVAN examined the structure of the non-stoicheiometric oxides.[9,10] They found that the compositions $CeO_{1.5}$ to $CeO_{1.53}$ had the A structure, and that this co-existed with material of C structure from $CeO_{1.53}$ to $CeO_{1.65}$; above $CeO_{1.8}$ both fluorite and rhombohedral structures were present. In the intervening region, BEVAN has suggested that a number of ordered phases were formed and that a rhombohedral phase co-existed with the C structure.[10] The oxygen dissociation pressures of the non-stoicheiometric oxides have been measured by BRAUER, using a dynamic method.[11] They ran from 10^{-17} to 10^{-23} atm over the temperature range of 650° to 1050°.

In observing the oxidation of cerium metal, LORIERS found the sesquioxide to be the initial oxide formed on the metal surface at room temperature.[12] Since then X-ray evidence has suggested that non-stoicheiometric oxides are formed before oxidation reaches the dioxide state.[13]

Praseodymium. The terpositive oxide Pr_2O_3, in contrast to that of cerium, is prepared at a lower temperature by reducing the non-stoicheiometric oxide with hydrogen at 600°. It is olive-green and dissolves readily in acids to give green praseodymium salts. The dioxide, PrO_2, has been made by treating this oxide with atomic oxygen,[14] and can also be obtained by heating it at 300° in oxygen at 50 atm pressure.[15] It has the fluorite structure.

The dioxide and the non-stoicheiometric oxides are dark coloured substances, varying from black to purple. When ignited in air at 800°, any of the oxides give material with the approximate composition Pr_6O_{11}.[16] This oxide dissolves in acids with evolution of oxygen to give terpositive salts.

It has been known for many years that the composition of praseodymium oxide varied with the oxygen pressure and temperature at the time of its preparation. The oxygen dissociation pressures have been measured by EYRING,[17,18] who found the isotherms were completely reversible, and a complete absence of hysteresis effects.

A high-pressure apparatus was used for preparing material with an oxygen content above $PrO_{1.85}$.[19]

The structure of the non-stoicheiometric oxides has been examined by X-ray powder photography; quenching techniques were checked with a high-temperature camera. This showed four structures in oxides ranging in composition from $PrO_{1.5}$ to $PrO_{1.85}$. The hexagonal lattice characteristic of lower oxygen content changes first to a body-centred cubic, then there is a rhombohedral region

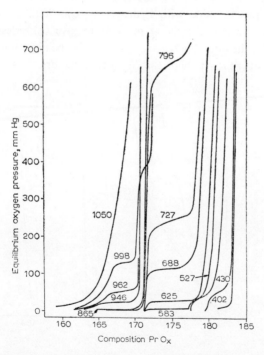

Fig. 12. Pressure–composition isotherms for praseodymium oxide. [Reproduced, with permission, from *J. Am. Chem. Soc.*, 76 (1954) 3890.]

References p. 96

from $PrO_{1.71}$ to $PrO_{1.77}$, followed by a face-centred cubic region. But above $PrO_{1.85}$ both face-centred cubic and fluorite phases are present. Generally similar conclusions on the range of structures were reached by BRAUER and MARTIN.[9, 20] However, oxygen dissociation pressures have recently been re-examined in the low pressure region[21, 22] by a more sensitive method; these gave evidence of hysteresis effects, which were attributed to the presence of domains of stable composition in the oxide.

The thermoelectric e.m.f. of praseodymium oxide–chromel junctions has been studied. These are positive with the oxide in hexagonal form, and negative when it is in the mixed phase region. When the junction is heated in air, its e.m.f. decreased and changed sign at 780°.[20]

Terbium. The terpositive oxide is prepared by reducing the non-stoicheiometric oxide with hydrogen at 600–800°. It is a cream coloured powder, dissolving in acids to give colourless terbium salts. The dioxide, TbO_2, was obtained by heating the oxide in atomic oxygen; it had the fluorite structure.[14] A range of

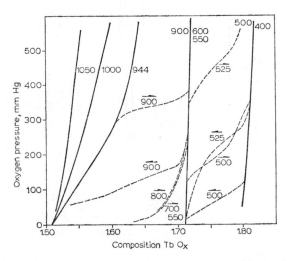

Fig. 13. Pressure–composition isotherms for terbium oxide. [Reproduced, with permission, from *J. Am. Chem. Soc.*, 76 (1954) 5242.]

non-stoicheiometric oxides result from the controlled oxidation of Tb_2O_3; they are brown and the material obtained by ignition in air at 800° approximates to the composition Tb_4O_7.[23] As with praseodymium, the non-stoicheiometric terbium oxides dissolve in acids with the evolution of oxygen to give terpositive salts.

The dissociation pressures of the non-stoicheiometric oxides have been measured by EYRING, who obtained reproducible isotherms above 900°, but observed a marked hysterisis, due to very slow attainment of equilibrium at lower temperatures.[24] X-ray examination showed a body-centred structure from $TbO_{1.5}$ to $TbO_{1.6}$, a rhombohedral structure at $TbO_{1.7}$, and a fluorite structure at $TbO_{1.81}$.[25] In an attempt to prepare the dioxide, the oxide was heated to 400° at an oxygen pressure of 282 atm; the product had, however, the composition $TbO_{1.86}$.[26]

LOWER OXIDES

Samarium, europium, and ytterbium. The sesquioxides of these elements are not reduced by hydrogen. However, several methods have been recently devised that originated with DAANE's preparation of the metals by the reduction of the oxides[27] (p. 129). To produce the lower oxide a number of reducing agents have been employed, the technique being to distil the more volatile lower oxide from the mixture of reactants and to condense it on a cold finger. EYRING prepared a lower oxide of samarium by heating samarium metal and sesquioxide in argon at 1100–1200°; the condensate had the composition $SmO_{0.5}$. It had the zincblende structure, and appeared to be an anion deficient oxide, it oxidised rapidly to the sesquioxide in air at 300°. The residue from the preparation of $SmO_{0.5}$ contained a red material with the sodium chloride structure. It was believed to be SmO, but the composition is still uncertain.[28]

The reduction of europium oxide with lanthanum metal was examined under similar conditions: at 1300°–1500°, an oxide of composition EuO vaporised, which also had the sodium chloride structure. Carbon and europium metal have also been used as reductants in this preparation.[29, 30] Magnetic measurements show the oxide to be bipositive.

The corresponding oxide of ytterbium, YbO, was made by reducing the sesquioxide with carbon.[31] It had the sodium chloride structure.

An unusual oxide of europium has been obtained by BRAUER, who heated a mixture of Eu_2O_3 and EuO at 900° in argon. It is dark red and has the empirical formula Eu_3O_4. Of interest is the isostructural compound, Eu_2SrO_4, made by heating Eu_2O_3 and strontium carbonate at 1000°.[32]

PROPERTIES OF THE RARE EARTH OXIDES

The oxides are the most important intermediates for rare earth preparations, since they are convenient starting points for most synthetic work by wet or dry methods. Reactivity depends on the thermal history of the oxide, and, when the most reactive material is required, pyrolysis should be carried out at the minimum temperature. Solution of the non-stoicheiometric oxides in acids is assisted by the addition of hydrogen peroxide, and with ceric oxide a very small quantity of hydrofluoric acid is helpful. The oxides melt at about 2000°, but individual melting points are not known accurately. The process of evaporation follows one of two mechanisms, depending on whether the oxide is that of a light or a heavy earth. The former dissociate to the monoxide and the latter to metal and oxygen.[33, 34]

$$Ln_2O_3 \rightarrow 2\,LnO + O$$

$$Ln_2O_3 \rightarrow 2\,Ln + 3\,O$$

The resistivity and thermoelectric power of some of the non-stoicheiometric cerium oxides has been examined[35] (p. 88). Conductivity measurements have also been made on a number of oxides and mixed oxide systems.[36]

Water–oxide equilibria

The hydration isotherms of a number of lanthanides were determined by WEISER. Neodymium and praseodymium both formed hydroxides of the type $Ln(OH)_3$, which dehydrated smoothly to the oxide.[37] SEITZ, using a hydrothermal treatment consisting of heating the oxide in steam, isolated crystalline $Ln(OH)_3$ and $LnO.OH$ which were characterised by X-ray examination.[38,39] ROY also applied hydrothermal techniques, but over a wider temperature and pressure range.[40] He isolated materials of composition $Ln(OH)_3$ and $LnO.OH$ under appropriate conditions. With yttrium, the oxide was the stable solid phase above 650°, but with La, Nd and Sm the behaviour was more complex. Within an appropriate pressure–temperature range, all gave two crystalline forms of the hydroxide $Ln(OH)_3$. Above 600–700° water vapour was in equilibrium with the anhydrous oxide. For Nd and Sm, this was the oxide with the *C* structure, but at 800–900°, that with the *B* structure was formed.

Mixed oxide systems

Binary systems of Ln_2O_3 oxides with LnO_2 oxides and with other quadripositive oxides have been studied. These investigations have been concerned with the theoretical problem of vacant anion lattices, and the more practical problem of stabilising refractory oxide materials such as thoria and zirconia.

McCULLOUGH examined a number of binary cerium–lanthanide systems.[15,41] The addition of the terpositive lanthanide oxide favoured a continuous change from the fluorite structure of ceria to the *C* form of the terpositive lanthanide. He found evidence of a miscibility gap at low Ln_2O_3 additions. A wider range of terpositive lanthanide additions to ceria and thoria was investigated by BRAUER.[42,43] Complete miscibility of the oxide systems was shown by Sm, Gd, Dy and Y, but miscibility gaps appeared with Nd and Yb. The partial miscibility with Yb is probably due to the difference in size of the M^{4+} and Yb^{3+} ions, but that with Nd arises from the instability of the C form of Nd_2O_3.

The stabilisation of zirconia with ceria and some tervalent lanthanide oxides has been studied by DUWEZ.[44,45]

COMPOUNDS OF RARE EARTH OXIDES
WITH OTHER METAL OXIDES

Two types of metal oxide compound, the titanates and the ferrites, have properties that have led to their application as electrical ceramics in the electronics industry. It is not surprising, therefore, that a large number of rare earth oxide–metal oxide systems have been investigated. The usual preparative method is to sinter together, in a vacuum or under a controlled atmosphere, a finely divided mixture of the two oxides in the required proportions.

The types of system that have been investigated are summarised in Table 15. Here, the usual nomenclature of designating the two metal ion species as A and B is followed. In the simplest case, the perovskite type of structure is formed between equimolar quantities of two oxides of stoicheiometry $AO_{1.5}$ and $BO_{1.5}$ provided that the tolerance factor t between the radii of the three ions A, B and O lies between 0.8 and 1. The tolerance factor t is given by the equation

$$t = \frac{R_A + R_O}{\sqrt{2}(R_B + R_O)}$$

where R_A, R_B, and R_O are the appropriate ionic radii.

It is also necessary for the two ions A and B to be large enough for 12-fold and 6-fold co-ordination respectively with oxygen.

With a perovskite type of structure, it is possible to substitute mixtures of ions for A or B, and various multiple ion substitutions have been discussed by ROY.[67] An example of this substitution is shown in Table 15, where a mixture of rare earth, niobium and barium ions is seen to have replaced the A^{3+} and B^{3+} ions.

TABLE 15

STRUCTURE OF RARE EARTH OXIDE–METAL OXIDE COMPOUNDS

Perovskite	ABO_3	Garnet	$A_3B_5O_{12}$	Scheelite	ABO_4
Compound	Ref.	Compound	Ref.	Compound	Ref.
$LnAlO_3$	46,47,48	$Ln_3Al_5O_{12}$	46	$LnGeO_4$	61
$LnCrO_3$	48,49,50	$Ln_3Ga_5O_{12}$	46	$LnNbO_4$	62
$LnCoO_3$	49,52	$Ln_3Fe_5O_{12}$	46	$LnTaO_4$	62,63
$LnGaO_3$	46				
$LnFeO_3$	48,51	Pyrochlore	$A_2B_2O_7$	Zircon	ABO_4
$LnMnO_3$	53	Compound	Ref.	Compound	Ref.
$LnNiO_3$	54				
$LnTiO_3$	55	$Ln_2Sn_2O_7$	58,59	$LnAsO_4$	64,65
$LnVO_3$	49,56	$Ln_2Zr_2O_7$	60	$LnPO_4$	65
$Ba(Ln,Nb)O_3$	57			$LnVO_4$	65,66

ROTH and SCHNEIDER have also shown that perovskites are formed between 1 : 1 mixtures of rare earth oxides, provided the tolerance factor is 0.79 or above.[68] When, however, the molar ratio between the two oxides is 3 : 5, the garnet structure $A_3B_5O_{12}$ is obtained. With B cations of greater charge number, compounds of the pyrochlore type have resulted, and ABO_4 compounds with the scheelite and zircon structures are known.

Usually, structural identification is by means of X-ray powder photographs. However, single crystals of the rare earth ferrites and garnets have been grown from melts, and structure determinations have been carried out on these.[69,70,71] The compounds have important magnetic properties.[72,73,74] The rare earth stannates also have interesting electrical properties.[75]

REFERENCES

Metal Oxides

1 V. M. GOLDSCHMIDT, F. ULRICH and T. BARTH, *Skrifter Norske Videnskaps Akad. Oslo*, 5 (1925) 1.
2 L. PAULING, *Z. Krist.*, 69 (1928) 415.
3 W. C. KOEHLER and F. O. WOLLAN, *Acta Cryst.*, 6 (1953) 741.
4 R. M. DOUGLASS and E. STARITZKY, *Anal. Chem.*, 28 (1956) 552.
5 D. T. CROMER, *J. Phys. Chem.*, 61 (1957) 753.
6 L. PAULING, *Z. Krist.*, 75 (1930) 128.
7 I. WARSHAW and R. ROY, *J. Phys. Chem.*, 65 (1961) 2048.
8 R. S. ROTH and S. J. SCHNEIDER, *J. Res. Nat. Bur. Std.*, 64A (1960) 309.
9 G. BRAUER and H. GRADINGER, *Z. Anorg. Allgem. Chem.*, 277 (1954) 89.
10 D. M. J. BEVAN, *J. Inorg. Nucl. Chem.*, 1 (1955) 49.
11 G. BRAUER, K. GINGERICH and U. HOLTSCHMIDT, *J. Inorg.Nucl. Chem.*, 16 (1960) 77.
12 R. COURTEL and J. LORIERS, *Compt. Rend.*, 230 (1950) 735.
13 J. LORIERS, *Compt. Rend.*, 231 (1951) 522.
14 C. M. GRUEN, W. C. KOEHLER and J. J. KATZ, *J. Am. Chem. Soc.*, 73 (1951) 1475.
15 J. D. McCULLOUGH, *J. Am. Chem. Soc.*, 72 (1950) 1386.
16 P. H. M. BRINTON and H. A. PAGEL, *J. Am. Chem. Soc.*, 45 (1923) 1460.
17 R. E. FERGUSON, E. D. GUTH and L. EYRING, *J. Am. Chem. Soc.*, 76 (1954) 3890.
18 E. D. GUTH, J. R. HOLDEN, N. C. BAENZIGER and L. EYRING, *J. Am. Chem. Soc.*, 76 (1954) 5239.
19 C. L. SIEGLAFF and L. EYRING, *J. Am. Chem. Soc.*, 79 (1957) 3024.
20 R. L. MARTIN, *Nature*, 165 (1950) 202.
21 J. M. HONIG, A. E. CLIFFORD and P. A. FAETH, *Inorg. Chem.*, 2 (1963) 791.
22 P. A. FAETH and A. E. CLIFFORD, *J. Phys. Chem.*, 67 (1963) 1453.
23 W. PRANDTL and G. REIDER, *Z. Anorg. Allgem. Chem.*, 238 (1938) 225.
24 E. D. GUTH and L. EYRING, *J. Am. Chem. Soc.*, 76 (1954) 5242.
25 N. C. BAENZINGER, H. A. EICK, H. SCHULETT and L. EYRING, *J. Am. Chem. Soc.*, 83 (1961) 2219.
26 W. SIMON and L. EYRING, *J. Am. Chem. Soc.*, 76 (1954) 5872.
27 A. H. DAANE, F. H. SPEDDING and D. H. DENNISON, *J. Am. Chem. Soc.*, 75 (1953) 2272.
28 H. A. EICK, N. C. BAENZINGER and L. EYRING, *J. Am. Chem. Soc.*, 78 (1956) 5147.
29 J. C. ACKLAND, *Bull. Soc. Chim.*, (1961) 31.
30 B. T. MATTHIAS, R. M. BOZORTH and J. VAN VLECK, *Phys. Review Letters*, 7 (1961) 160.
31 J. C. ACKLAND and G. TSOUCONS, *Compt. Rend.*, 246 (1958) 285.
32 H. BARMINGHANSEN and G. BRAUER, *Acta Cryst.*, 15 (1962) 1059.
33 H. W. GOLDSTEIN, P. N. WALSH and J. WHITE, *J. Phys. Chem.*, 65 (1961) 1400.
34 M. B. PARISH, *J. Chem. Phys.*, 34 (1961) 1079; 2197.
35 A. W. CZENDERRE and J. M. HONIG, *Phys. Chem. Solids*, 6 (1958) 96.

36 L. Noddak, H. Walsh and W. Dobner, Z. Physik. Chem., 211 (1959) 180; 194.
37 H. B. Weiser and W. O. Milligan, J. Phys. Chem., 42 (1938) 673.
38 K. Schubert and A. Seitz, Z. Naturforsch., 1 (1946) (6) 321.
39 R. Fricke and A. Seitz, Z. Anorg. Allgem. Chem., 254 (1947) 107.
40 M. W. Shafer and R. Roy, J. Am. Ceram. Soc., 42 (1959) 563.
41 J. D. McCullough and J. Britton, J. Am. Chem. Soc., 74 (1952) 5225.
42 G. Brauer and H. Gradinger, Z. Anorg. Allgem. Chem., 276 (1954) 209.
43 G. Brauer and H. Gradinger, Naturwiss., 38 (1957) 559.
44 P. Duwez and F. Odell, J. Am. Ceram. Soc., 33 (1950) 274.
45 P. Duwez, F. Brown and F. Odell, J. Electrochem. Soc., 98 (1951) 356.

Metal oxide compounds

46 F. Bertaut and F. Forrat, Compt. Rend., 243 (1956) 1219.
47 S. Geller and V. Bala, Acta Cryst., 9 (1956) 1019.
48 A. Ruggiero and R. Ferro, Gazz. Chim. Ital., 85 (1955) 892.
49 A. Wold and R. Ward, J. Am. Chem. Soc., 76 (1954) 1029.
50 S. Quezel-Ambruinez and M. Mareschal, Bull. Soc. Franc. Mineral. Cryst., 86 (1963) 204.
51 H. Forestier and G. Guiot-Guillain, Compt. Rend., 230 (1950) 1844.
52 A. Wold, B. Post and E. Banks, J. Am. Chem. Soc., 79 (1957) 6365.
53 R. C. Vickery and A. Klann, J. Chem. Phys., 27 (1957) 1161.
54 A. Wold, B. Post and E. Banks, J. Am. Chem. Soc., 79 (1957) 4911.
55 E. I. Krylov, Zh. Neorgan. Khim., 1 (1956) 366.
56 V. A. Naumov, Zh. Strukt. Khim., 3 (1962) 608.
57 L. Brixner, J. Inorg. Nucl. Chem., 15 (1960) 352.
58 C. G. Whinfrey, D. W. Eckhart and A. Tauber, J. Am. Chem. Soc., 82 (1960) 2695.
59 C. G. Whinfrey and A. Tauber, J. Am. Chem. Soc., 83 (1961) 755.
60 R. C. Vickery and A. Klann, J. Chem. Phys., 27 (1957) 1220.
61 F. Bertaut and A. Durif, Compt. Rend., 238 (1954) 2173.
62 H. P. Rooksby and E. A. D. White, Acta Cryst., 16 (1963) 888.
63 E. I. Krylov and M. Pinaeva-Strelina, Zh. Neorgan. Khim., 8 (1963) 2254.
64 A. Durif and F. Forrat, Compt. Rend., 245 (1957) 1636.
65 H. Schwarz, Z. Anorg. Allgem. Chem., 323 (1963) 44.
66 A. Durif, Acta Cryst., 9 (1956) 471.
67 R. Roy, J. Am. Ceram. Soc., 37 (1954) 581.
68 S. J. Schneider and R. Roth, J. Res. Nat. Bur. Std., 64A (1960) 317.
69 J. P. Remeika, J. Am. Chem. Soc., 78 (1956) 4259.
70 J. W. Neilsen and E. F. Dearborn, Phys. Chem. Solids, 5 (1958) 202.
71 S. Geller and E. Wood, Acta Cryst., 9 (1956) 563.
72 M. A. Gilleo, J. Chem. Phys., 24 (1956) 1239.
73 M. A. Gilleo and S. Geller, Phys. Review, 110 (1958) 73.
74 R. Aleonard, J. C. Barbier and R. Pauthenet, Compt. Rend., 242 (1956) 2531.
75 S. Marzullo and E. N. Bunting, J. Am. Ceram. Soc., 41 (1958) 40.

CHAPTER 9

Sulphides, Selenides and Tellurides

When oxygen is replaced by larger atoms such as sulphur, selenium, or tellurium, a wider range of compounds is obtained. In most cases, four types of chalcogenides and one oxochalcogenide have been identified. The preparation of a number of these compounds involves experimental difficulties; methods are described below. Sometimes the stoicheiometry of the compounds is not well established, and most of the systems have at least one range of variable composition. Few of the crystal stuctures of the compounds are known; and, although phase transitions have been clearly demonstrated, very few transition temperatures are yet precisely known.

RARE EARTH SULPHIDES

Preparation

Monosulphides LnS

1. Direct union of the elements. The reaction is carried out in a sealed tube, containing separated reactants; the temperature is slowly increased, and held at $1000°$.[1,2]

$$Ln + S \rightarrow LnS.$$

2. Reduction of the sesquisulphide with aluminium. The reaction mixture is first heated to $1000°–1200°$ to produce the intermediate sulphide Ln_3S_4. This, when heated at $1500°$ under 10^{-2} mm pressure, is reduced to the monosulphide from which aluminium sulphide sublimes.[3]

$$9 \text{ Ln}_2S_3 + 2 \text{ Al} \rightarrow 6 \text{ Ln}_3S_4 + \text{Al}_2S_3$$

$$3 \text{ Ln}_3S_4 + 2 \text{ Al} \rightarrow 9 \text{ LnS} + \text{Al}_2S_3$$

3. Reaction between the metal hydride and sesquisulphide. The reaction is carried out at 1800°–2200° and 10^{-4}–10^{-5} mm pressure.[4]

$$\text{CeH}_3 + \text{Ce}_2S_3 \rightarrow 3 \text{ CeS}$$

4. Electrolysis of the sesquisulphide in a fused salt bath. A mixture of cerium trichloride and sesquisulphide is electrolysed in a NaCl–KCl eutectic at 800°, at a potential of 5 V. The reduction is believed to involve the initial formation of cerium metal, which dissolves in the electrolyte and there reduces the sesquisulphide.[5]

$$\text{Ce}_2S_3 \rightarrow \text{Ce}_3S_4 \rightarrow \text{CeS}$$

Europium monosulphide cannot however be prepared by any of these methods. It is made by passing H_2S over the heated trichloride.[10]

$$2 \text{ EuCl}_3 + 3 \text{ H}_2S \rightarrow 2 \text{ EuS} + 6 \text{ HCl} + S$$

The sulphides Ln_3S_4

1. Direct union of mono- and sesquisulphides. A mixture of the two sulphides is heated at 1500–1600° in a graphite crucible in a vacuum.[4, 6]

$$\text{LnS} + \text{Ln}_2S_3 \rightarrow \text{Ln}_3S_4$$

2. Reduction of the sesquisulphide with aluminium. Formation occurs when the reactants are heated at 1100–1200°; the temperature is then increased to 1500° to distil off the aluminium sulphide.[3]

$$9 \text{ Ln}_2S_3 + 2 \text{ Al} \rightarrow 6 \text{ Ln}_3S_4 + \text{Al}_2S_3$$

3. Reaction between the metal hydride and sesquisulphide. The mixture is heated at 400° in a stream of H_2S, and the product is then raised to 2000° in a vacuum.[4] So far the method has been used for the cerium compound only.

$$\text{CeH}_3 + 4 \text{ Ce}_2S_3 \rightarrow 3 \text{ Ce}_3S_4 + 1.5 \text{ H}_2$$

The europium and samarium compounds cannot be obtained by

any of these methods. The europium compound is prepared by heating the monosulphide with the requisite quantity of sulphur in a sealed tube at 600° for some days.[7]

$$3 \, EuS + S \rightarrow Eu_3S_4$$

The samarium compound results from the dissociation of either the disulphide or sesquisulphide in a vacuum at 1800°.[8]

$$Sm_2S_3 \, (or \, SmS_2) \rightarrow Sm_3S_4 + S$$

Sesquisulphides Ln_2S_3

1. Reaction of H_2S with a halide salt. For this purpose the H_2S must be rigorously dried, and the reaction controlled so that the temperature remains below the melting point of the halide. Except for europium, this method is of general application.[9, 10]

$$3 \, H_2S + 2 \, LnCl_3 \rightarrow Ln_2S_3 + 6 \, HCl$$

2. Reaction of H_2S and the oxide. Again the H_2S used must be rigorously dried. The reaction appears to be initiated at 550° with the formation of oxosulphides; the preferred technique is to operate at 1250–1300° in a graphite boat.[8, 11, 12]

$$3 \, H_2S + Ln_2O_3 \rightarrow Ln_2S_3 + 3 \, H_2O$$

The oxides of three elements behave exceptionally under these conditions. Thus when ceric oxide is used, the product must be heated with graphite to complete the reaction. Europium oxide yields the monosulphide. A lower reaction temperature (800°–1100°) must be used to obtain ytterbium sesquisulphide.[13]

3. Thermal dissociation of the disulphides. This is carried out at a temperature of 600° or above, in a vacuum.[8]

$$2 \, LnS_2 \rightarrow Ln_2S_3 + S$$

Disulphides LnS_2

1. Reaction of the sesquisulphide and sulphur. The reaction, in a sealed tube at 600°, lasts for several days.[14] For the preparation of the europium compound the monosulphide is used.[13]

$$Ln_2S_3 + S \rightarrow 2\ LnS_2$$

2. Reaction of the anhydrous sulphates with H_2S. This reaction takes place at 500–600° and the sulphides of La, Pr, and Nd have been prepared in this manner, but oxosulphides would appear to be likely contaminants.[10,15]

Oxosulphides Ln_2O_2S
1. Direct union of oxide and sesquisulphide. A mixture with a 20% excess of sulphide, is heated in a graphite boat at 1350° in a vacuum for 3 h. The excess of sulphide is removed by leaching the product with 10% acetic acid.[16,17] For the preparation of the europium oxosulphide, the reaction requires the sulphide and sulphur in the proportions EuS: 0.5 S, to be heated with the oxide.[7]

$$2\ Ln_2O_3 + Ln_2S_3 \rightarrow 3\ Ln_2O_2S$$

2. Reaction between the oxide and H_2S at 550–600°. The product contains some sulphide, which is removed by leaching with 10% acetic acid.[17]

$$Ln_2O_3 + H_2S \rightarrow Ln_2O_2S + H_2O$$

3. Partial hydrolysis of the sesquisulphide at 500°.[3] Hydrogen is used as the carrier gas, careful control of the proportion of steam being essential.

$$Ln_2S_3 + 2\ H_2O \rightarrow Ln_2O_2S + 2\ H_2S$$

4. Reaction of the oxides with thioacetamide at 1200°. The product is heated in air at 800° to oxidise any impurities. Ten oxosulphides have been prepared by this route.[18]

$$Ln_2O_3 + MeCSNH_2 \rightarrow Ln_2O_2S + \text{side products}$$

Double sulphides containing Ln_2S_3
Double oxides of the rare earth elements of the ABO_3 type are well known (p. 94). Here, A is the rare earth and B is another terpositive metal.

Double sulphides of the rare earths with aluminium or gallium have been prepared. A mixture of the sulphides is heated in a graphite boat over which a stream of H_2S is passed. The reaction temperature is 1200–1250° for the aluminium compounds and 1000° for the gallium compounds. Aluminium salts have been made for a number of the rare earths. The lanthanum and yttrium gallium sulphides have also been prepared.[19]

$$Ln_2S_3 + Al_2S_3 \xrightarrow{H_2S} 2LnAlS_3$$

The cubic (γ) form of the sesquisulphides gave a series of solid solutions with the sulphides of barium, calcium and strontium, which also have a cubic structure. The solid solutions extend between the compositions Ln_2S_3 and MLn_2S_4, where M is the alkaline earth cation. Magnesium and manganese sulphides also form solid solutions, but over a smaller range of composition.[20]

Structure of the rare earth sulphides

The monosulphides
The structures are of the cubic NaCl type. With the exception of Eu and Sm, lattice parameters decrease in accordance with the lanthanide contraction.[1,23,24] Parameters of the salts from La to Nd are independent of the preparative route; the salts are well defined compounds. Magnetic measurements on the La, Ce, Nd and Y compounds show the lanthanides to be terpositive; this implies an unbonded electron and metallic type conduction.[21,22]

In contrast, europium and samarium in their monosulphides are both bipositive on the magnetic evidence. Ytterbium forms a non-stoicheiometric range in the region of YbS, which is probably due to ytterbium vacancies in the lattice. In material of composition YbS ytterbium is bipositive, but in material represented by YbS_{1+x} some of the ytterbium is terpositive and has a smaller ionic radius. This change in radius together with an increase in lattice vacancies results in YbS_{1+x} having a smaller lattice parameter than YbS.[12]

The sulphides Ln_3S_4

The structures are cubic, and of the Th_3P_4 type, with four molecules to the unit cell. Lattice dimensions for the La to Nd salts are very close to those of the sesquisulphides, but their densities show that the salts are not mixtures of Ln_2S_3 and LnS. Magnetic measurements show the lanthanide in them to be terpositive; again, an unbonded electron gives metallic type conductivity.[8,23,24]

The unit cells of both the samarium and europium sulphides are larger than expected from the parameters of neighbouring salts. Magnetic measurements show that both bi- and terpositive cations are present, which explains the size difference. Incidentally the electrical conductivity of both compounds is low compared with others of this type.

The sesquisulphides Ln_2S_3

Four forms have been found in the rare earth sesquisulphides, but the structure of only two of these, the γ and δ forms, are established with certainty. Some similarity may be expected to the transformations of the rare earth oxides, but the transformation temperatures between the various structures are not known with sufficient precision for a comparison to be useful. The ranges of stability so far defined are summarised in Table 16.

With the La–Nd group, the γ form can be obtained at all temperatures, but the β form is often produced below 1000°. With samarium

TABLE 16

STRUCTURE OF RARE EARTH SESQUISULPHIDES

Temp.	La	Ce	Pr	Nd	Sm	Gd	Dy	Y
1500	γ	γ	γ	γ	γ			δ
1400		β						
1200	β	β						
1100		α	β	β	γ	γ	δ	
1000			α,β	α	α			
850	β	α	α	α	α			δ
800	β					α	α	

and gadolinium, the γ form is obtained above 1000–1100°. Erbium and ytterbium only give the δ form. The structures of the α and β forms are unknown. The γ form is cubic, derived from the Th_3P_4 structure by cation vacancies.[8,23,24] This form is known for the light lanthanides and dysprosium; the 'a' parameter decreases regularly with atomic number. The δ structure is complex. Measurements on single crystals of Er_2S_3 showed it to be monoclinic; the unit cell contains 6 molecules.[8] Ytterbium sesquisulphide has an unusual structure; it is probably orthorhombic.

The disulphides LnS_2
The composition of the light earth disulphides, those from La to Nd, corresponds to LnS_2. But the higher lanthanide salts are deficient in sulphur, and prolonged heating with the element fails to increase its proportion above $LnS_{1.9}$. Magnetic measurements show the lanthanide ions to be terpositive, hence the compounds are true polysulphides. Ce and Pr are both 4-coordinate in their dioxides, but this grouping is prevented in the disulphides by the size of the sulphur atoms.

The La to Sm group has tetragonal structures of an unknown type. Sulphides with sulphur below $LnS_{1.8}$ have lines characteristic of both cubic and tetragonal structures. Density determinations show the tetragonal phases to have anion vacancies.

The oxosulphides Ln_2O_2S
Magnetic measurements on a number of these compounds show the lanthanide to be terpositive. They have a hexagonal structure, and both the 'a' and 'c' parameters vary regularly with the size of the terpositive ionic radius.[16,17]

Properties of the rare earth sulphides

The monosulphides LnS
Reliable data are available on the cerium compound only. Its melting point is 2450°, and it has a vapour pressure of 10^{-3} mm at 1900°. The heat of formation is -117.9 kcal/mole. It dissolves

sulphur at high temperatures, and forms an eutectic melting at
2000° with the sulphide Ce_3S_4.[4]

The sulphides Ln_3S_4

The melting points of the La–Nd compounds are over 2000°.
That of Sm_3S_4 is 1800°; it begins to volatilise at 1600°. These
compounds are less volatile than the sesquisulphides. For the
cerium compound the heat of formation (-421.5 kcal/mole) and
resistivity (4×10^{-4} ohm cm) have been determined.[4]

The sesquisulphides Ln_2S_3

The melting points of a number of these compounds have been
determined and sometimes those of different crystal forms of the
same compound. For these determinations the material is supported
on an inert refractory, usually TiC or ZrC.

The sesquisulphides have an appreciable vapour pressure at the
melting point. The samarium compound readily dissociates at
1800° and leaves Sm_3S_4, that of yttrium goes to Y_5S_7 at 1700° and
of ytterbium similarly to Yb_5S_7 at 1000°. With compounds which
do not dissociate below that temperature there is little attack on
carbon below 1750°. When heated with aluminium in a vacuum,
the light earth sulphides are slowly reduced to compositions
intermediate between Ln_2S_3 and Ln_3S_4. But the heavy earths and
ytterbium are reduced at 1300° to sulphides of the composition
Ln_5S_7, and at higher temperatures to monosulphides.

When a sesquisulphide is heated with its oxide at 1350° the
oxosulphide Ln_2O_2S is formed. The sulphides are oxidised in
air at 500° to basic sulphates.

TABLE 17

MELTING POINTS OF SESQUISULPHIDES (°C)

Crystal form	La	Ce	Pr	Nd	Sm	Gd	Dy	Er	Y
γ	2080	2060	1795	2010	1780	1885	1490		
β	1915	1700	1775						
δ							1470	1730	1600

The disulphides LnS_2

The disulphides dissociate in a vacuum above 600° to give the sesquisulphides. On heating in air, the disulphides of Ce, Pr, Nd and Sm are oxidised to basic sulphates.

The oxosulphides Ln_2O_2S

These are oxidised in air above 600° to form the basic sulphates and are reduced by carbon above 1500°.

Chemical properties of the sulphides

The compounds are stable in dry air, but there is some hydrolysis in moist air at room temperature with the evolution of H_2S. They are oxidised when heated in air to the basic sulphate; oxidation commences at 200–300°. The sulphides are more readily oxidised than the corresponding selenides or tellurides.

The sulphides are insoluble in water, and inert to nitrogen and CO_2 at high temperatures. They are all attacked by acids, with the evolution of H_2S, but on the Ln_3S_4 sulphides and the oxosulphides the attack is slower.

RARE EARTH SELENIDES

Four types of selenide, and one of oxoselenide, have been prepared; their compositions are the same as that of the corresponding sulphur compound.

Monoselenides LnSe

1. Direct union of the elements. These are heated in a sealed tube at 950–1000°.[25,26]

$$Ln + Se \rightarrow LnSe$$

2. Reduction of the oxide and sesquiselenide with aluminium metal. The reactants are heated in graphite in a vacuum. When heated to 1350°, the product contains the selenide Ln_3Se_4 as well as LnSe. On further heating to 1700°, reduction to the monoselenide is com-

plete, and aluminium and its lower oxide evaporate from the preparation.[27]

$$Ln_2O_3 + 2\ Ln_2Se_3 + 3\ Al \rightarrow 6\ LnSe + 3\ AlO \uparrow$$

3. Reduction of the sesquiselenide with sodium or calcium. The method was used for preparing the cerium compound. The reactants were heated in a sealed tube, at 600° for sodium and at 1000° for calcium.[28]

$$Ce_2Se_3 + 2\ Na \rightarrow 2\ CeSe + Na_2Se$$

The monoselenides have the cubic sodium chloride structure. Measurement of the lattice parameters and densities show somewhat less selenium than required for the stoicheiometric composition, usually about $LnSe_{0.95}$. Magnetic measurements indicate that the lanthanide ions are terpositive; the compounds are therefore subselenides with an unbonded electron.[27] To this, europium, samarium and ytterbium are exceptions. The europium compound may be prepared by reaction of H_2Se on the oxide or trichloride.[27,29,30] Samarium sesquiselenide dissociates on heating at 1700° in a vacuum to the monoselenide, and the ytterbium compound may be prepared by hydrogen reduction of the sesquiselenide at 1250°.[27,30] The magnetic properties of these three compounds show the lanthanide ions to be bipositive and they have salt-like properties.[27,30]

Sesquiselenides Ln_2Se_3

1. Reaction between H_2Se and the oxide or chloride. Temperatures of 1000° are used for the oxides and 600–800° for the chlorides. This is a general route and most of the sesquiselenides have been prepared in this way.[29]

$$Ln_2O_3 + 3\ H_2Se \rightarrow Ln_2Se_3 + 3\ H_2O$$

$$2\ LnCl_3 + 3\ H_2Se \rightarrow Ln_2Se_3 + 6\ HCl$$

2. Direct union of the elements. Reaction is carried out in a sealed tube, a lower temperature (800°) being used than in the monoselenide preparation.[26,28,31]

$$2\,Ln + 3\,Se \rightarrow Ln_2Se_3$$

3. Dissociation or reduction of the diselenides. The light earth diselenides (Ln–Nd) dissociate at 1200°, but the gadolinium compound gives the sesquiselenide at 800°.[32]

$$2\,LaS_2 \xrightarrow{\;1200°\;} La_2Se_3 + Se$$

The sesquiselenides have a cubic structure of the Th_3P_4 type, with a deficiency of cations. For the light earths (La–Nd), there is a range of variable stoicheiometry from $LnSe_{1.33}$ to $LnSe_{1.50}$ in which the material has a cubic structure.[32] The lattice parameters of both compositions vary with the radius of the terpositive lanthanide ion.

Diselenides $LnSe_2$

1. Reaction between the sesquiselenide and selenium in a sealed tube at 600°.[26]

$$Ln_2Se_3 + Se \rightarrow 2\,LnSe_2$$

2. Heating the metal in a stream of H_2Se. The reaction temperature is increased to 1250° over a period of 9 h.[33]

$$Ln + 2\,Se \rightarrow LnSe_2$$

The diselenides, from La to Gd, have a range of composition from $LnSe_{1.8}$ to $LnSe_2$. They have a tetragonal structure with four molecules per unit cell. Magnetic measurements show the lanthanide ions to be terpositive. When heated in a vacuum at 500–700°, they slowly lose selenium, and at compositions below $LnSe_{1.8}$ the cubic Ln_2Se_3 phase appears.

Oxoselenides Ln_2O_2Se

1. Reaction of the oxide and sesquiselenide for 2 h at 1350° under reduced pressure.[34]

$$2\,Ln_2O_3 + Ln_2Se_3 \rightarrow 3\,Ln_2O_2Se$$

2. Partial selenation of the oxide at 1000° in a mixture of hydrogen and H_2Se.[34, 35]

$$Ln_2O_3 + H_2Se \rightarrow Ln_2O_2Se + H_2O$$

The oxoselenides have a hexagonal structure, which resembles that of the oxosulphides. They are more stable chemically than the normal selenides. When heated with aluminium at 1350°, they are reduced to the monoselenides.

RARE EARTH TELLURIDES

Some members of five different types of telluride have been prepared, namely LnTe, Ln_3Te_4, Ln_2Te_3, $LnTe_2$, and Ln_2O_2Te.

The monotellurides LnTe
1. Direct union of the elements. The reaction is carried out in a sealed tube, the temperature being increased to a maximum of 1000–1100°.[36-40]

$$Ln + Te \rightarrow LnTe$$

This method has been used for the light earths and yttrium.
2. Reduction of the sesquitelluride with hydrogen at 950°.[41]

$$Yb_2Te_3 + H_2 \rightarrow 2 YbTe + H_2 + Te$$

This method was used for ytterbium, but did not succeed with samarium.
3. Reaction of tellurium on the halide.[42] The approach is confined to europium.

$$4 EuCl_3 + 7 Te \rightarrow 4 EuTe + 3 TeCl_4$$

The monotellurides have been stated to possess a cubic NaCl structure but some recent work has not confirmed this view.[43]

The tellurides Ln_3Te_4
Dissociation of the ditelluride in a vacuum at 950–1100°.[44, 45]

$$3 LnTe_2 \rightarrow Ln_3Te_4 + 2 Te$$

The product has the Th_3P_4 structure.

The sesquitellurides Ln_2Te_3

Direct union of the elements. Reaction is carried out in a sealed tube, at a maximum temperature of $950°$.[38,40,45]

$$2 Ln + 3 Te \rightarrow Ln_2Te_3.$$

The light earth sesquitellurides have the cubic Th_3P_4 structure.[46]

The ditellurides $LnTe_2$

Direct union of the elements. The reaction temperature is 550–600°.[44,47]

$$Ln + 2 Te \rightarrow LnTe_2$$

The light earth ditellurides are tetragonal, having the Fe_2As structure. They dissociate in a vacuum at $400°$ with the loss of tellurium; the composition approaches Ln_3Te_4 which has a cubic structure.[48]

The oxotellurides Ln_2O_2Te

The reaction of tellurium with the lanthanide oxide at $1000°$.[43,49] With hydrogen as a carrier gas, somewhat lower temperatures may be used.[50]

$$2 Ln_2O_3 + 2 Te \rightarrow Ln_2O_2Te + TeO_2$$

The La–Dy compounds have been prepared in this way; they have a tetragonal structure.[43] These materials are very resistant to chemical attack, but dissolve slowly in aqua regia and in molten caustic soda. They are slowly oxidised when heated in air, with the progressive replacement of tellurium by oxygen.

Single crystals of some of the light earth sesqui- and ditellurides have been prepared. The sesquitelluride and iodine were sealed in an evacuated silica tube, and a $300°$ temperature gradient was applied to the tube. After ten days growth, crystals of both compounds had formed in different parts of the tube. The ditellurides had a tetragonal structure; electrical measurements along the crystal axes showed anisotropic thermoelectric effects.[51,52]

CONCLUSIONS

Sulphur, selenium and tellurium all form compounds of similar composition with the lanthanide elements. In the three types of compound there are two ranges of variable stoicheiometry from Ln_3X_4 to Ln_2X_3, and again from $LnX_{1.8}$ to LnX_2. There are also certain common structural features, thus the LnX, Ln_3X_4 and Ln_2X_3 compositions have a cubic structure, which tends to be obscured in the case of the sesquisulphides by polymorphism. The LnX_2 compounds are tetragonal, and the oxocompounds Ln_2O_2X are hexagonal or tetragonal.

FLAUHAUT has suggested that the chalcogenides of composition Ln_2X_3 fit into five structures, which are summarised in Table 18.[53]

TABLE 18

SUGGESTED STRUCTURES OF Ln_2X_3 COMPOUNDS

	La	Ce	Pr	Nd	Sm	Gd	Dy	Y	Er	Yb	Lu
Te					η						ζ
Se		γ									
S							δ			ε	

γ Cubic structure Th_3P_4 type; η Orthorhombic, posibly Sb_2S_3 type; δ Monoclinic, structure unknown; ζ Unknown structure; ε Hexagonal, structure unknown.

In view of the large volume of work on these compounds in the past ten years, it is disappointing that only one of these structures is known.

REFERENCES

Sulphides

1 I. IANDELLI, *Gazz. Chim. Ital.*, 85 (1955) 881.
2 I. IANDELLI, *Z. Anorg. Allgem. Chem.*, 288 (1956) 81.
3 J. FLAUHAUT and E. ATTAL, *Compt. Rend.*, 238 (1954) 682.

4 E. D. EASTMAN, L. BREWER, L. A. BROMLEY, P. W. GILLES and N. L. LOF-GREN, *J. Am. Chem. Soc.*, 72 (1950) 2248.
5 R. DIDCHENKO and L. M. LITZ, *J. Electrochem. Soc.*, 109 (1962) 247.
6 M. PINCON and J. FLAUHAUT, *Compt. Rend.*, 243 (1956) 2074.
7 L. DOMANGE, J. FLAUHAUT and M. GUITTARD, *Compt. Rend.*, 249 (1959) 687.
8 M. PINCON, J. FLAUHAUT, L. DOMANGE, M. GUITTARD and M. PATRIE, *Bull. Soc. Chim.*, (1960) 221.
9 W. KLEMM and J. J. ROCKSTROH, *Z. Anorg. Allgem. Chem.*, 163 (1927) 253.
10 W. KLEMM, K. MEISEL and H. VOGEL, *Z. Anorg. Allgem. Chem.*, 190 (1930) 123.
11 J. FLAUHAUT, M. GUITTARD and M. PATRIE, *Bull. Soc. Chim.*, (1958) 990.
12 J. FLAUHAUT and M. GUITTARD, *Compt. Rend.*, 243 (1956) 1210.
13 L. DOMANGE, J. FLAUHAUT, M. GUITTARD and J. LORIERS, *Compt. Rend.*, 247 (1958) 1614.
14 J. FLAUHAUT, M. GUITTARD and M. PATRIE, *Bull. Soc. Chim.*, (1959) 1917.
15 W. BLITZ, *Z. Anorg. Allgem. Chem.*, 71 (1911) 427.
16 J. FLAUHAUT and M. GUITTARD, *Compt. Rend.*, 241 (1955) 1775.
17 M. PICON and M. PATRIE, *Compt. Rend.*, 242 (1956) 516.
18 H. A. EICK, *J. Am. Chem. Soc.*, 80 (1958) 43.
19 L. DOMANGE, J. FLAUHAUT and M. PATRIE, *Bull. Soc. Chim.*, (1960) 229.
20 J. FLAUHAUT, L. DOMANGE, M. PATRIE, A. M. BOSTSARRON and M. GUITTARD, *Adv. Chem. Ser.*, 39 (1963) 179.
21 J. FLAUHAUT and M. GUITTARD, *Compt. Rend.*, 242 (1956) 1319.
22 M. PICON and M. PATRIE, *Compt. Rend.*, 242 (1956) 1321.
23 W. H. ZACHARIASEN, *Acta Cryst.*, 1 (1948) 265.
24 W. H. ZACHARIASEN, *Acta Cryst.*, 2 (1949) 57; 291.

Selenides

25 I. IANDELLI, *Gazz. Chim. Ital.*, 85 (1955) 881.
26 J. F. MILLER, F. J. REID and R. C. HIMES, *J. Electrochem. Soc.*, 106 (1959) 1043.
27 M. GUITTARD and H. BENACERRAF, *Compt. Rend.*, 248 (1959) 1959.
28 E. BANKS, K. F. STRIPP, H. W. NEWKIYK and R. WARD, *J. Am. Chem. Soc.*, 74 (1952) 2450.
29 W. KLEMM and A. KOCZY, *Z. Anorg. Allgem. Chem.*, 233 (1937) 84.
30 W. KLEMM and H. SENFF, *Z. Anorg. Allgem. Chem.*, 241 (1937) 259.
31 M. GUITTARD, J. FLAUHAUT and L. DOMAGE, *Compt. Rend.*, 256 (1963) 427.
32 A. BENACERRAF and M. GUITTARD, *Compt. Rend.*, 248 (1959) 2012.
33 A. BENACERRAF, L. DOMANGE and J. FLAUHAUT, *Compt. Rend.*, 248 (1959) 1672.
34 A. BENACARRAF, M. GUITTARD, L. DOMANGE and J. FLAUHAUT, *Bull. Soc. Chim.*, (1959) 1920.
35 H. A. EICK, *Acta Cryst.*, 13 (1960) 161.

Tellurides

36 A. IANDELLI, *Gazz. Chim. Ital.*, 85 (1955) 881.
37 A. IANDELLI, *Z. Anorg. Allgem. Chem.*, 288 (1956) 81.
38 J. F. MILLER, R. REID and R. C. HIMES, *J. Electrochem. Soc.*, 106 (1959) 1043.
39 L. H. BRIXNER, *J. Inorg. Nucl. Chem.*, 15 (1960) 199.
40 J. F. MILLER, L. K. MATSON and R. C. HIMES, *Rare Earth Research*, ed. C. E. LUNDIN, Macmillan, New York, 1962, p. 233.
41 H. SENFF and W. KLEMM, *Z. Anorg. Allgem. Chem.*, 242 (1939) 92.
42 W. KLEMM and H. SENFF, *Z. Anorg. Allgem. Chem.*, 241 (1939) 259.
43 M. P. PARDO, J. FLAUHAUT and J. DOMANGE, *Compt. Rend.*, 255 (1960) 937.
44 L. DOMANGE, J. FLAUHAUT, P. PARDO, A. N. CHIRAZI and M. GUITTARD, *Compt. Rend.*, 250 (1960) 857.
45 M. PARDO, J. FLAUHAUT and L. DOMANGE, *Compt. Rend.*, 256 (1963) 1793.
46 J. FLAUHAUT, L. DOMANGE, M. GUITTARD, M. P. PARDO and M. PATRIE, *Compt. Rend.*, 257 (1963) 1530.
47 M. P. PARDO, J. FLAUHAUT and L. DOMANGE, *Compt. Rend.*, 256 (1963) 1793.
48 A. BENACERRAF and M. GUITTARD, *Compt. Rend.*, 248 (1959) 2012.
49 L. DOMANGE, J. FLAUHAUT and A. N. CHIRAZI, *Bull. Soc. Chim.*, (1959) 150.
50 R. A. KENT and H. A. EICK, *Inorg. Chem.*, 1 (1962) 956.
51 P. BRO, *J. Electrochem. Soc.*, 109 (1962) 1110.
52 J. C. ANDRELLOS and P. BRO, *Solid-State Electron.*, 5 (1962) 414.
53 J. FLAUHAUT, L. DOMANGE, M. GUITTARD, M. P. PARDO and M. PATRIE, *Compt. Rend.*, 257 (1963) 1530.

CHAPTER 10

Analytical methods

As most of the lanthanide elements appear in solution as particularly stable 3+ ions, few classical methods are available for the determination of individual elements. However, both volumetric and gravimetric procedures are applicable to cerium, and there is a volumetric method for europium. Volumetric and gravimetric procedures are also available for assessing the total lanthanide content and for ascertaining the mean equivalent weight.

Usually it is necessary to rely upon physical methods for the determination of individual lanthanides. Undoubtedly, spectrophometry is the most important of these; on the other hand, polarography has only a limited application. Emmission spectroscopy is the most sensitive criterion of purity. X-ray fluorescent spectroscopy is most valuable in the determination of yttrium. Ion-exchange elution methods are used for the separation of rare earth fission products.

CLASSICAL METHODS

Determination of cerium. Gravimetric procedure. The method depends upon the quantitive precipitation of ceric iodate, $Ce(IO_3)_4$, which is finally weighed as ceric oxide.[1] The analytical solution initially contains cerium as Ce^{3+}. To this an excess of ammonium iodate is added; the mixture is heated to 70–80⁰ in the presence of ammonium persulphate. The cerium, precipitated quantitatively as iodate, is filtered off, fumed with sulphuric acid and ignited. The residue of cerium dioxide is weighed.

Determination of cerium. Volumetric procedure. The methods rely upon a quantitative oxidation of cerium from the 3+ to the 4+ state. Depending on the other anions in the solution, the potential of the Ce^{4+}/Ce^{3+} couple varies from 1.3 to 1.9 V.[2]

Oxidation to the 4+ state may be brought about by either sodium bismuthate or silver-catalysed sodium persulphate.[3,4] The ceric ion is reduced back to the 3+ state by titration with a reducing agent, usually a standard ferrous iron solution, in the presence of an indicator of the phenanthroline type.

$$Ce^{4+} + Fe^{2+} \rightarrow Ce^{3+} + Fe^{3+}$$

Determination of europium. Volumetric procedure. Europium is reduced quantitatively to the bipositive state by passing an acidified solution (pH 3–4) of its salt through a Jones reductor.[5] The europous ion in the effluent is oxidised quantitatively to the 3+ state by a standard solution of either iodine or potassium dichromate.

$$2 \, Eu^{2+} + I_2 \rightarrow 2 \, Eu^{3+} + 2 \, I^-$$

The original europium solution must be free from oxidising agents and sulphate ions.

Total lanthanides. Gravimetric procedure. The solubilities of the lanthanide oxalates are of the order of 10^{-6} moles/l, and oxalate precipitation is probably the best procedure available for the quantatitive isolation of the elements.[6] A 25% excess of oxalic acid is added to a cold, dilute lanthanide solution, and the pH adjusted to 2.0 with either ammonia or nitric acid. The precipitate is coarsened by heating for 1–2 h; it is filtered off and ignited in platinum at 800–900° to the oxide. Unless precipitation is carried out from strongly acidic solutions, normal oxalates of the light earths and yttrium are obtained. However, with the heavy earths, the precipitate is a mixture of the normal oxalate and a double ammonium oxalate[7] (p. 46).

When the oxalates are ignited, they are converted to Ln_2O_3 oxides except for cerium, which gives the dioxide, CeO_2, and praseodymium and terbium, which have non-stoicheiometric oxides approximating in composition to Pr_6O_{11} and Tb_4O_7. The last two oxides are reduced to Pr_2O_3 and Tb_2O_3 respectively by heating in hydrogen at 500–600°, but ceric oxide is more resistant to reduction (p. 85).

When the analytical solution contains large quantities of added salts, mixed oxalate precipitates such as sulphate–oxalates are precipitated, which do not pyrolyse to the oxide at the temperature used for igniting the oxalates. In these circumstances, it is advisable first to precipitate the lanthanide hydroxides with ammonia, and, after washing, to dissolve the precipitate in the minimum of nitric acid, and finally to separate as oxalate in the normal manner.

Total lanthanides. Volumetric procedure. The lanthanon elements all form negatively charged complex anions with ethylenediamine tetraacetic acid[8] (pp. 33 and 57).

$$Ln^{3+} + Y^{4-} \rightarrow LnY^{-1}$$

The association constants for these reactions are large, and there is a great fall in the lanthanide ion concentration at the equivalence point. As EDTA is a weak acid, its ionisation depends on the hydrogen ion concentration of the solution. For analytical purposes, it is clearly necessary to buffer the solution so that reproducible changes in metal ion concentration at the equivalence point can be obtained.

If the solution is buffered to pH 7 with triethanolamine, it is then possible to titrate with a standard EDTA solution to an Eriochrome BlackT end point.[9] An alternative method, which depends on the specificity of the Zincon indicator for zinc, is to add an excess of standard EDTA to the triethanolamine-buffered rare earth solution. The excess of EDTA is determined by back-titrating with a standard zinc solution to a Zincon end point.

Determination of mean equivalent weight. Two classical methods are available; they are the sulphate–oxide and the oxalate–oxide.[10, 11] In the first, lanthanide oxalates are converted to the anhydrous sulphates by fuming with concentrated sulphuric acid. The sulphates produced are weighed and then heated above 1000° when pyrolysis to the oxide takes place.

$$Ln_2(Ox)_3 \rightarrow Ln_2(SO_4)_3 \rightarrow Ln_2O_3$$

In the second method, a portion of the lanthanide oxalate precipitate is dissolved in hot sulphuric acid, and the oxalate titrated with standard permanganate. A second portion of oxalate is ignited to the oxide. As mentioned earlier, this method is only reliable for the light earths and yttrium.[7] Clearly, when non-stoicheiometric oxides are formed on ignition, both methods suffer from the disadvantages of the gravimetric procedure.

INSTRUMENTAL METHODS

Absorption spectroscopy. With the exception of lanthanum, lutetium and yttrium, all of the lanthanide elements absorb light in the visible and near-visible region. With one exception, namely, solutions of $3+$ and $4+$ cerium, the elements show a series of narrow, sharply-defined peaks well suited for analytical purposes, the spectra being characteristic of the metal cations. Complexing agents can, however, affect the magnitude of the molar absorptivity and must be absent from the analytical solutions.[12]

Determinations are usually made on chloride or perchlorate solutions and it is important that analytical solutions should be free from interfering substances such as ferric iron or free chlorine. Cerium, both cerous and ceric, has a very strong and broad absorption band in the ultra-violet region and must be previously removed from analytical solutions. The absorption spectra of the lanthanides have been observed in some detail by PRANDTL and SCHEINER.[13] Extinction coefficients obtained with modern recording instruments are summarised in Table 19.[14, 15] Data on promethium have been obtained by MEGGERS.[16] The absorption spectra of many of the lanthanide elements display more than one 'analytical peak', and when te peaks coincide

TABLE 19

MOLAR ABSORPTIVITIES OF THE RARE EARTH ELEMENTS

Wave-length mµ	Molar absorptivity, l/mole cm										
	Pr	Nd	Sm	Eu	Gd	Tb	Dy	Ho	Er	Tm	Yb
219.8					320						
272.8	1.13	0.210	0.166	0.335	*4.20*		0.215	0.227	0.698	0.685	0.365
287.0	0.511	0.185		0.132			0.140	*3.59*	0.316	0.521	0.266
350.4		2.60	0.052				*2.54*	0.057	0.096	0.145	
354.0		*5.20*	0.087				0.737	0.047	0.382	0.454	
361.1		0.042	0.453	0.053			0.271	2.34	0.296	0.801	
365.0		0.025	0.244	0.062			*2.10*	0.331	1.94	0.154	
379.6		0.067	0.052	0.299			0.252	0.047	*7.18*		
394.2		0.025	0.148	*3.06*			0.233	0.123	0.096		
401.5			*3.31*	0.097			0.187	0.038	0.086		
444.2	*10.49*		0.044				0.047	0.454	0.306		
450.8	1.29	0.025					0.261	*4.16*	0.497		
521.6		*4.41*						0.047	2.10		
523.5		1.68						0.076	*3.20*		
537.0								*5.16*	0.076		
575.5	0.102	*6.93*									
640.4								*3.53*	0.153		
683.0		0.336								*2.56*	
739.5		7.20								0.058	
794.0		*11.78*					0.084		0.143	0.579	
908.0							*2.46*	0.113			0.089
974.0			0.052				0.047		1.29		*2.12*

with background absorption by other lanthanides there is mutual interference. Clearly, the absorption of the solution at any 'analytical peak' is the sum of the absorption of each element at that wavelength. When complex mixtures are examined, the concentration of the individual elements may be determined by solving a series of simultaneous equations; solutions by successive approximation are usually sufficiently accurate. The observations are preferably made on a double beam instrument; indeed this procedure is essential for the accurate determination of gadolinium and terbium.

Polarography. The potentials of the couples Eu^{3+}/Eu^{2+} and Yb^{3+}/Yb^{2+} are 0.43 and 1.15 V respectively. In both, reduction at the dropping mercury electrode is quantitative and the step height proportional to the lanthanide concentration. The method is quantitative with ammonium chloride as the base electrolyte.[17,18] When derivative polarography is employed, less than 5 p.p.m. of either element may be detected.

The reduction of samarium (III) to the bipositive Sm^{2+} is observed at an e.m.f. (1.35 V) above that of the hydrogen wave, and is unsuitable for quantitative work.[19] Similar reduction steps are observed with the other lanthanides but they too are unsuitable for quantitative work.

Emission spectroscopy. Two general methods are available. For the analysis of complex mixtures of lanthanides, such as complete assemblages extracted from minerals, the 'iron flux' method may be used.[20] The unknown material is mixed with a ferric sulphate flux, and a range of standard dilutions is prepared.

Samples of these are evaporated from copper electrodes in a D.C. arc, and the rare earth spectra are superimposed on an iron reference spectrum. Lines characteristic of the rare earths are identified by visual comparison. For quantitative assessment, line densities are determined with a microphotometer and compared with standard plates prepared from mixtures of known composition.

The second method, due to FASSEL, is used for concentrates carrying large quantities of one rare earth element.[21] Here, very conveniently, the major or matrix element provides the reference spectrum. Samples are mixed with graphite and evaporated from carbon electrodes in a D.C. arc. A carbon dioxide atmosphere is used to suppress cyanogen bands. The spectrum is compared with the spectra of a series of standards containing known quantities of neighbouring elements, and quantitative determinations are similar to those made by the iron-flux method.

The main experimental difficulty in emission spectroscopy arises from inter-element interference, the reason for which is obscure.

References p. 123

The fact is that certain combinations of lanthanides cause line enhancement or line suppression. The effects are most marked in multi-component systems, but become considerably less important as the purity of the sample is increased. In consequence, the precision of the iron-flux method for multi-component systems is probably not better than $\pm$ 20%. At the other extreme, although the sensitivity of the Fassel method varies from one rare earth element to another, the detection limits of lanthanide impurities lies in the range 0.01% to 0.001%.

X–ray fluorescent spectroscopy. In this technique, the analytical sample forms a target for white radiation from an X-ray source. The target atoms emit their characteristic K or L radiation, which are the Moseley spectra characteristic of the atomic number of the elements. The emitted radiation is collected, usually on a bent crystal and, after collimation, is detected with a Geiger or scintillation counter placed at the Bragg angle. For the rare earth elements, the L spectra are used and are excited by radiation from a tungsten target.

There are various inter-element effects which can enhance or suppress lines. The most important of these effects is due to the absorption edge of the elements; this is at a lower wavelength than the Moseley lines, and, like them, decreases in wavelength with atomic number. An absorption edge can attenuate radiation emitted by elements of higher atomic number. As a result the method of X-ray fluorescent spectroscopy is complex in practice, and it is essential to compare the unknown sample with a matrix of similar composition. However, yttrium is an exception; since its atomic number is 18 lower than the nearest rare earth it can be determined readily. The K spectra are used in this case, excitation being with radiation from a molybdenum target. The application of this technique to complex lanthanide fractions has been described.[22,23]

Separation of the rare earth elements from uranium and thorium. As some of the rare earth elements have very large neutron-capture cross-sections, methods for separating and determining the relatively small quantities of them in nuclear grades of uranium and thorium have been developed. The uranium or thorium concentrate is dissolved in nitric acid and transferred quantitatively to a chromatographic column charged with activated cellulose. When eluted with a diethylether–nitric acid solvent (5% v/v nitric acid for uranium, and 12.5% v/v nitric acid for thorium), these elements are removed from the column to leave the rare earths and other impurities at the top of the column. The rare earths are then eluted with 2–3 N hydrochloric acid, and precipitated as oxalates in the presence of a calcium carrier. After further chemical separation, the rare earths are determined gravimetrically, and then examined spectroscopically by the iron-flux method.[24]

The analysis of fission products. This is carried out by ion-exchange chromatography in which the elution technique is used with a solution of a complexing agent. The principle is the same as that involved in the macroscopic scale separations described in Chapter 3, and depends upon differences in the affinity of individual rare earth cations for the complexing agent. The quantity of rare earth present in solution to which separations are applied is very small, usually less than 0.1% of the total exchange capacity of the resin, and there are a number of important differences in technique.

A typical elution chromatogram is shown in Fig. 14. When a mixture of cations, A, B, at the top of a chromatographic column is eluted with a solution of another cation with less affinity for the

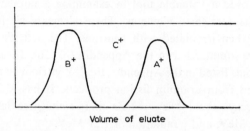

Volume of eluate

Fig. 14. Elution.

resin, the cations are separated by the elution into a series of Gaussian peaks.[25] The ion of lowest affinity is actually the ammonium cation and the different rates of movement of the rare earth ions through the column are caused by differences in the affinity of these ions for the complexing agent. When the rare earth loading on the column is small, only small changes in the eluant pH are produced by the complexing reaction. Elution is carried out on an NH_4^+/H^+ form column, and, in order to separate the elements, it is necessary to have sufficient rare earth in cationic form to provide reflux between the resin and the aqueous phase. In practice, this is done by careful control of the eluant pH.

Solutions of hydroxyacids are usually employed in this type of separation. Classical separations were carried out with ammonium citrate solutions (pH 3.2–3.4) in a column 1 m long, maintained at 100°.[26] The elution took 30 h to complete under optimum conditions. By using resins of smaller particle size and lower cross-linking, it is possible to scale down the size of the separation column and complete an elution in a few hours. A variety of hydroxyacids have been used for this purpose, for instance lactic, glycollic, and α-hydroxyisobutyric.[27,28,29] A gradient elution technique has also been used with an ammonium lactate eluant; the eluant pH was increased by 0.1 pH unit/h, and this gave a very effective separation.[30]

RADIOACTIVE LANTHANIDES

Tracers have proved a valuable tool in examining a number of properties of the rare earth elements. These elements all form active isotopes when irradiated with neutrons. The activities of these isotopes are summarised in the Appendix (p. 156). In addition to the materials listed in the Appendix, the ^{91}Y yttrium isotope is readily isolated from uranium fission products. It has a 58 d half-life, and decays thus: $^{91}Y \rightarrow {}^{91}Zr$ st. It emits β radiation of 0.32 and 1.35 MeV, and γ radiation of 1.21 MeV.

CONCLUSIONS

To sum up, a variety of precise methods are available for determining the purity of individual rare earth elements. The precision rapidly falls off with more complex mixtures, and is far from satisfactory for the complete lanthanide assemblages isolated from minerals. For these materials, the methods available are only semi-quantitative. Although excellent methods have been developed for separating the rare earth elements from nuclear materials, the individual lanthanides can be determined only by the same semi-quantitative methods.

REFERENCES

1 H. H. WILLARD and S. T'SAI YU, *Anal. Chem.*, 25 (1953) 1754.
2 E. WADSWORTH, F. R. DUKE and C. A. GOETZ, *Anal. Chem.*, 29 (1957) 1824.
3 F. METZGER, *J. Am. Chem. Soc.*, 31 (1909) 523.
4 H. H. WILLARD and P. YOUNG, *J. Am. Chem. Soc.*, 50 (1928) 1322.
5 H. N. MCCOY, *J. Am. Chem. Soc.*, 57 (1935) 1756.
6 L. A. SARVER and P. H. M. BRINTON, *J. Am. Chem. Soc.*, 49 (1927) 943.
7 M. F. BARRETT, T. R. R. MCDONALD and N. E. TOPP, *J. Inorg. Nucl. Chem.*, 26 (1964) 931.
8 G. SCHWARZENBACH and E. FREITAG, *Helv. Chim. Acta*, 34 (1951) 1503.
9 H. FLASCHKA, *Mickrochim. Acta*, (1955) 55.
10 G. URBAIN, *J. Chem. Phys.*, 4 (1906) 52.
11 W. GIBBS, *Proc. Am. Acad.*, 28 (1893) 261.
12 R. C. VICKERY, *J. Mol. Spectr.*, 2 (1958) 308.
13 W. PRANDTL and K. SCHEINER, *Z. Anorg. Allgem. Chem.*, 220 (1934) 107.
14 C. V. BANKS and D. W. KLINGMAN, *Anal. Chim. Acta*, 15 (1956) 356.
15 E. I. ONSTOTT and C. J. BROWN, *Anal. Chem.*, 30 (1958) 172.
16 W. F. MEGGERS, B. F. SCRIBNER and W. R. BOZMAN, *J. Res. Nat. Bur. Std.*, 46 (1951) 85.
17 H. N. MCCOY, *J. Am. Chem. Soc.*, 58 (1936) 1577.
18 H. A. LAITINEN and W. A. TAEBEL, *Ind. Eng. Chem. (Anal. Ed.)*, 13 (1941) 825.
19 A. TIMNICK and G. GLOCKLER, *J. Am. Chem. Soc.*, 70 (1948) 1347.
20 *Springfields Chemical Sevices, Method No. 357*, (1954).
21 V. A. FASSEL, H. D. COOK, L. C. KROTZ and P. W. KEHRES, *Spectrochim. Acta*, 5 (1952) 201.
22 R. H. HEIDEL and V. A. FASSEL, *Anal. Chem.*, 30 (1958) 176.
23 F. W. LYTLE and H. H. HENDRY, *Anal. Chem.*, 31 (1959) 809.

24 G. H. SMITH, *Revised handbook of chemical and physical methods for the determination of uranium and thorium in minerals*, N.C.L. Pub. H.M.S.O., 1955.
25 A. J. P. MARTIN and M. L. SYNGE, *Biochem. J.*, 35 (1941) 1358.
26 B. H. KETELLE and G. E. BOYD, *J. Am. Chem. Soc.*, 69 (1947) 2800.
27 J. G. CUNINGHAME, N. H. SIZELAND, H. H. WILLIS, J. EAKINS and E. MERCER, *J. Inorg. Nucl. Chem.*, 1 (1955) 163.
28 D. C. STEWART, *Anal. Chem.* 27 (1955) 1279.
29 G. R. CHOPPIN and R. J. SILVA, *J. Inorg. Nucl. Chem.*, 3 (1956) 153.
30 W. E. NERVIK, *J. Phys. Chem.*, 59 (1955) 690.

CHAPTER 11

The rare earth metals

Preparation of the rare earth metals in a pure state is difficult for a number of reasons. The metals have a wide range of melting points, from 800° to 1650°, and they are exceedingly reactive when molten. This raises the two problems of confinement and containment, and makes the task of minimising contamination from gas and solid phase formidable.

Most of the experimental work has been concentrated upon two methods, electrolysis from fused salt baths, and the metallothermic reduction of oxides or halides, usually the latter. In theory, a third approach should be feasible, namely electrodeposition from non-aqueous solvents, but this has not yet received a systematic examination. Electrodeposition from aqueous solution is, of course, ruled out by the reactivity of the metals.

ELECTROLYSIS FROM FUSED SALT BATHS

Two types of fused salt electrolysis have been used: in one the electrolyte is a trihalide, in the other an oxide. The bath usually consists of a fused salt eutectic, held at a temperature above the melting point of the metal. For many years, the properties of the available refractories and the small supply of heavy rare earth materials have limited electrolytic extraction to the lower-melting light earth materials.

Halides. These salts were employed as far back as 1875 by HILLEBRAND and NORTON.[1] However, the lanthanum, cerium and neodymium metals produced by KRAMERS even forty years ago were probably grossly contaminated by being alloyed with other metals

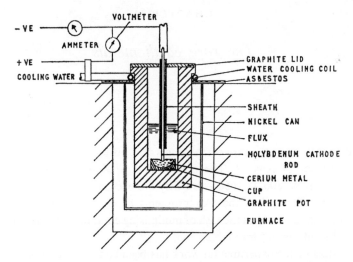

Fig. 15. Cell for electrolysis of fused cerium trichloride. [Reproduced, with permission, from *Bull. Inst. Mining Met.*, 61 (1951) 141.]

produced during the electrolysis.[2, 3] Advances in technique were brought in by TROMBE, notably by the introduction of carbon and molybdenum refractories; moreover, the deliberate production of alloys was used in the isolation of some of the higher melting metals.[4, 5, 6] Trombe's preparation of cerium metal has been repeated in the cell shown diagrammatically in Fig. 15.[7]

Anhydrous cerous chloride was dissolved in a molten potassium chloride–cerous fluoride flux (4.5 mole% CeF_3) at a working temperature of 850°. A sheathed molybdenum rod formed the cathode, the graphite crucible being the anode. When the solution was electrolysed at 4.5–5.5 V with a current density of 3–4 A/cm², the current efficiency in terms of metal produced was of the order of 70%*. Control of the current was critical; both higher and lower densities caused a metal dispersion into the electrolyte and a fall

---

* Current density is the current per unit area of the working electrode; the efficiency of an electrode process is expressed as a percentage of the theoretical yield calculated from the Faraday law.

in yield. The purest metal obtained was 99.7%; a small contamination derived from cell materials could not be completely avoided.

Oxides. The electrolysis of ceric oxide in molten cerium fluoride was originally tried by MUTHMANN,[8] and has also been re-examined by GRAY.[7] Ceric oxide dissolved to the extent of 5% in an electrolyte consisting of a ternary mixture of cerium, lithium, and barium fluorides in the molar proportions 20 : 75 : 5. The most satisfactory electrodes proved to be a molybdenum cathode and a graphite anode, and the metal produced was collected in a molybdenum crucible immersed in the electrolyte (Fig. 16).

The working temperature was 880–900°, with a current density of 5–7 A/cm². Examination of the off-gases showed that loss from the graphite anode corresponded to the formation of carbon dioxide at its surface. The procedure gave cerium of 99.7–99.8% purity.

Both methods show promise, particularly the oxide electrolysis, and work is now in progress to develop them further. The operation

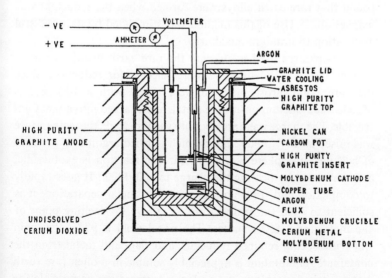

Fig. 16. Cell for electrolysis of cerium dioxide dissolved in fused fluorides. [Reproduced, with permission, from *Bull. Inst. Mining. Met.*, 61 (1951) 141.]

is essentially that already described, but rigorous attemps are being made to exclude water vapour from the cell, and to limit the attack of molten metal on the cell liner by protecting the latter with a layer of frozen electrolyte. The effectiveness of both of these approaches is facilitated by working on a larger scale.[9, 10]

METALLOTHERMIC REDUCTION METHODS

Reduction of a rare earth halide with an alkali or alkaline earth metal has been frequently used for the preparation of the metals. The method is of general application except for samarium, europium and ytterbium, where reduction by these means leaves the element in the bipositive state.

$$LnX_3 + 3 M \rightarrow Ln + 3 MX$$
$$LnX_3 + M \rightarrow LnX_2 + MX \text{ (for Sm, Eu, Yb)}$$

KLEMM used reduction with the alkali metals,[11, 12] and TROMBE found that rare earth alloys were formed when the reductant was magnesium.[13] Use of this method was stimulated by its successful application to uranium metallurgy.

The apparatus used to prepare the rare earth metals is shown in Fig. 17.[14, 15] The fluorides were selected for reduction, since they are non-hygroscopic, and were mixed with a 10% excess of redistilled calcium or lithium metal, and charged into a tantalum crucible. The charge was outgassed in a vacuum while the temperature was raised slowly to 600°, after which purified argon to a pressure of half an atmosphere was admitted. The reaction is exothermic, and is initiated by heating the charge to 800–1000°. It goes rapidly to completion and, to obtain a good slag–metal separation, it is sufficient to hold the temperature 50° above the melting point of the metal for a few minutes. The metal yield is 97%, the main impurities being retained reductant and slag, and metal from the container. As tantalum is appreciably soluble in molten rare earth metals, it is desirable to use as low a temperature as possible for the reduction.

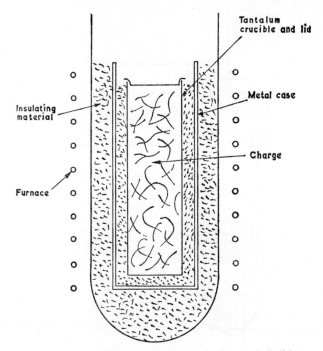

Fig. 17. Metallothermic reduction of rare earth halides.

A different technique is used for the preparation of samarium, europium and ytterbium. These three metals have an abnormally high vapour pressure, and this is exploited to reduce them with lanthanum metal.[16,17]

$$Sm_2O_3 + 2\,La \rightarrow La_2O_3 + 2\,Sm$$

The vacuum apparatus used for these preparations is shown in Fig. 18.

The rare earth oxide, mixed with a 10% excess of lanthanum metal turnings, is heated in a high vacuum in a tantalum container. The volatile metal is collected in a tantalum condenser maintained at a lower temperature by a resistance furnace. Control of the temperature of the condenser is important in obtaining the metal as a suitably crystalline deposit. Because of its relatively high

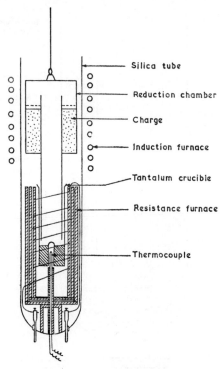

Fig. 18. Preparation of europium metal. [Reproduced, with permission, from *Trans. A.I.M.E.*, 212 (1958) 378.]

volatility, the deposited metal does not contain detectable amounts of lanthanum or tantalum. A further advantage of the vacuum technique is that the O, N, and H impurities are also low (<100 p.p.m.).

DISTILLATION OF THE RARE EARTH METALS

Metals prepared by calcium or lithium reduction contain occluded reactants and tantalum, besides contaminants derived from the vapour phase. The more volatile impurities are readily removed by distillation, but metal oxides and tantalum remain in the still.[18]

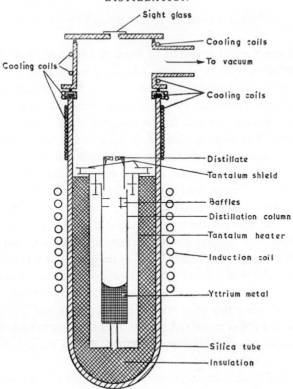

Fig. 19. Distillation of rare earth metals. [Reproduced, with permission, from *J. Less-Common Metals*, 5 (1963) 134.]

The apparatus is shown in Fig. 19. For successful operation, rigorous outgassing of the charge is needed, and it is convenient to carry out the distillation at a metal vapour pressure of 1–2 mm. The physical form of the product is controlled by the condenser temperature, which is adjusted to give crystalline material. This may be consolidated into ingots by arc-melting on a water-cooled copper hearth. Impurities such as calcium, oxygen, and tantalum are <100 p.p.m.

PURIFICATION OF THE RARE EARTH METALS

A rare earth metal prepared by thermal reduction, and purified by distillation, retains as impurities of importance O, N and H. Three ways of further purification have been examined. The zone-refining technique in a horizontal boat was not effective because the molten metal is contaminated by material from the container. The floating zone technique overcame the difficulty of containment but effected little separation of the impurities. Another method was to pass currents of several hundred amperes through bars of metal, held in an inert atmosphere and maintained at a temperature about 200° below the melting point. After treatment for 50 h, some migration of metallic and oxygen-containing impurities was observed with cerium and yttrium, but other impurities were not affected.[19, 20] The third method was to extract molten metal with a fused salt. For instance, yttrium was reduced with magnesium to give a low-melting (950°) yttrium–magnesium alloy, and when this alloy was stirred with a molten YF_3–$CaCl_2$ eutectic there was a marked reduction in the oxygen and fluoride contents of the metal.[21] The mechanism of the second of these processes is unknown.

None of these techniques offers much promise of improving the purity of the product. We are forced to conclude that most chance of preparing the pure metals lies in further refinement of the reduction processes themselves.

Metal single crystals

The preparation of single crystals of yttrium has been described by SPEDDING.[22] A cylinder, 2 cm diameter by 3 cm, was cut from an arc melted ingot of yttrium, made by thermal reduction. After being vacuum annealed for 24 h at 1200°, the whole cylinder had been converted into a single crystal. The method has been successful with a number of the metals.[23] Such crystals have been used for measuring changes in resistivity with temperature along the crystal axes.

Preparation of intermediates

The rare earth metals are usually obtained from an anhydrous salt. These salts are very hygroscopic, and hydrolyse readily, and their preparation in a suitable moisture free condition calls for ingenuity.

Chlorides. These salts hydrolyse readily to form the oxide chlorides. The hydrolysis reaction has been studied by CUNNINGHAM.[24, 25] It can be limited in extent by heating the hydrated salt in a stream of HCl gas, or with solid ammonium chloride. Dry reactions between the oxide and phosgene or carbon tetrachloride can be used, careful temperature control being necessary to avoid fusion of the rare earth salt which prevents further reaction. In all cases, some oxide halide or unreacted oxide remains, and the halide can be separated from this only by vacuum distillation.

The rare earth bromides and iodides have lower melting and boiling points than the chlorides. However, their preparation in an anhydrous state is more difficult, since the halogen acids disproportionate readily and, moreover, these halides appear to hydrolyse more readily than the chlorides.

Fluorides. The fluorides are precipitated from aqueous solution as gelatinous hydrates, but these hydrolyse to the oxide fluoride on drying. To overcome this difficulty, a dry reaction between the oxide and anhydrous HF or ammonium bifluoride is employed. The reaction is normally carried out in Monel equipment at 700°, and fluidization techniques have been examined for scaling up the process. Even under the best conditions, it is extremely difficult to attain complete conversion to the fluoride. Thus prepared, the fluorides are non-hygroscopic. Before reduction to metal, they need a complete outgassing; nevertheless, residual oxygen is still a major impurity in the metal.

PROPERTIES OF THE RARE EARTH METALS

Melting and boiling points, latent heat, compressibilities and atomic volumes

These properties are summarised in Table 20.

References p. 141

The melting points were determined either by thermal arrest, or by observing with an optical pyrometer the appearance of liquid in a hole drilled in a small metal ingot. Boiling points and latent heats of fusion were deduced from vapour pressure measurements made by the Knudsen effusion technique. Usually, more than one set of measurements, in reasonably good agreement, is available. The atomic volumes given in Table 20 relate to the form of metal stable at room temperature.

When plotted against atomic number, the atomic volume steadily decreases, as is expected from the lanthanide contraction, and the melting point increases (Fig. 20). Marked anomalies are shown by europium and ytterbium, especially for melting point, atomic volume and radius, latent heat of fusion and compressibility. When these properties are compared with those of neighbouring metals in the periodic system, europium and ytterbium show the behaviour displayed by many bipositive metals. For this reason, europium and

TABLE 20

PHYSICAL PROPERTIES OF THE RARE EARTH METALS

Element	Atomic Number	Melting Point	Boiling Point	Latent heat, kcal/mole	ρ g/ml	Atomic volume ml/mole	Compressibility cm²/kg × 10²
Y	39	1509	2927	93	4.478	19.86	—
La	57	920	3469	96	6.174	22.50	3.9
Ce	58	795	3468	95	6.771	20.695	4.7
Pr	59	935	3127	79	6.782	20.778	3.7
Nd	60	1024	3027	69	7.004	20.60	3.0
Sm	62	1072	1900	46	7.536	19.97	3.5
Eu	63	826	1349	42	5.259	28.91	7.0
Gd	64	1312	3000	72	7.895	19.88	2.5
Tb	65	1356	2800	70	8.272	19.245	—
Dy	66	1407	2600	67	8.536	19.032	2.6
Ho	67	1461	2600	67	8.803	18.742	2.5
Er	68	1497	2900	67	9.051	18.473	2.5
Tm	69	1545	1727	59	9.332	18.151	2.6
Yb	70	824	1427	38	6.997	24.80	7.5
Lu	71	1652	3327	99	9.842	17.78	—

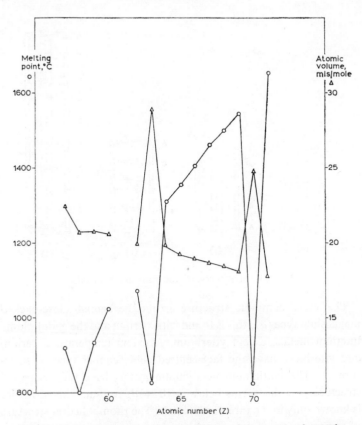

Fig. 20. Melting points and atomic volumes of the rare earth metals.

ytterbium metals are considered to be bipositive. The low-temperature form of cerium (below$-150°$) also has an anomalous atomic volume and effective magnetic moment; these anomalies are in the opposite sense to those found with europium and ytterbium. This form of metal (α-cerium) is thought to be quadripositive.

Crystal structure and transformations of the metals. The four crystal structures of the metals at room temperature (excepting cerium) are shown diagrammatically in Fig. 21.

References p. 141

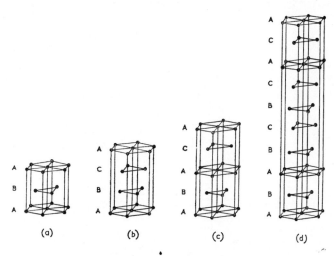

Fig. 21. Structures of the rare earth metals.

The most common structure is the hexagonal close-packed magnesium type *(a)*; this is found with yttrium and the gadolinium–lutetium metals, except ytterbium. At room temperature, cerium and ytterbium have the face-centred cubic copper type of structure*(b)*. The lanthanum–neodymium metals have the hexagonal structure *(c)*; this forms below $-10°$ with cerium. This structure is known only in the rare earth metals. The rhombohedral structure of samarium *(d)* is unique.

The more important crystallographic information about the metals is summarised in Table 21. Many of the metals have several crystalline forms, and although the transition temperatures of some

TABLE 21

CRYSTALLOGRAPHIC DATA OF THE RARE-EARTH METALS

Element	Temperature range	Structure	Lattice constants, Å	Atomic radius, Å
Y	to 1495	h.c.p.	a 3.3080 c 5.2653	1.801
	> 1495	b.c.c.	a 4.11	

(Table 21 continued)

Element	Temperature range	Structure	Lattice constants, Å	Atomic radius, Å
La	—271 to 310	hex	a 3.770	1.877
			c 12.131	
	310 to 868	f.c.c.	a 5.303	
	> 868	b.c.c.	a 4.26	
Ce	—150	f.c.c.	a 4.85	
	—150 to —10	hex	a 3.68	
			c 11.92	
	—10 to 730	f.c.c.	a 5.1604	1.825
	> 730	b.c.c.	a 4.12	
Pr	to 798	hex	a 3.6702	1.828
			c 11.828	
	> 798	b.c.c.	a 4.13	
Nd	to 868	hex	a 3.6582	1.821
			c 11.802	
	> 868		a 4.13	
Sm	to 917	rhomb.	a 8.996	1.802
Eu	to 826	b.c.c.	a 4.578	2.042
Gd	to 1262	h.c.p.	a 3.6315	1.802
			c 5.777	
	> 1262	?	a 4.06	
Tb	to 1310	h.c.p.	a 3.5900	1.782
			c 5.696	
Dy	to 950	h.c.p.	a 3.5923	1.773
			c 5.6545	
Ho	to 966	h.c.p.	a 3.5761	1.766
			c 5.6174	
Er	to 917	h.c.p.	a 3.5590	1.757
			c 5.592	
Tm	to 1004	h.c.p.	a 3.5372	1.746
			c 5.5619	
Yb	to 798	f.c.c.	a 5.481	1.940
	> 798	b.c.c.	a 4.44	
Lu	to 1400	h.c.p.	a 3.5050	1.734
			c 5.5486	

References p. 141

TABLE 22

HEATS OF FORMATION OF THE RARE EARTH OXIDES

Oxide	$-\Delta H, 25°$ kcal/mole	Ref.
Y_2O_3	455.5	38
La_2O_3	428.6	39
Ce_2O_3	435	39
Pr_2O_3	436.8	40
Nd_2O_3	432.1	41
Sm_2O_3	433.9	42
Gd_2O_3	433.9	43
Tb_2O_3	436.8	44
Dy_2O_3	445.8	45
Ho_2O_3	449.5	46
Er_2O_3	453.6	45
Tm_2O_3	451.8	47
Yb_2O_3	433.7	45
Lu_2O_3	452.8	47

of these changes have been determined, a complete structural picture is not yet available.[28,29]

Heats of formation of oxides. The heats of combustion of the rare earth metals have been determined (Table 22). The similar element yttrium has a higher heat of formation than any of the rare earth elements. The magnitude of the heats of formation is evidence that the metals are strongly electropositive.

Resistivity. The resistivity of the rare earth metals has been studied over a wide temperature range, in some cases from 1–1000° K; in a number of investigations single crystal specimens were examined. At room temperature, the resistivities of the metals lie between 50 and 150 μohm/cm. Compared with copper or aluminium, the rare earth metals have resistivities from one to two orders of magnitude higher; thus they are relatively poor conductors of electricity. All have a positive temperature coefficient of resistivity. Discontinuities are found at structural and magnetic transition temperatures.

Lanthanum metal becomes a superconductor below 5° K; this

property has also been found among certain rare earth alloys with indium and with the platinum metals (p. 151). [30,31]

Magnetic properties. The effective magnetic moments of the metals (except for Ce, Eu and Yb) agree very closely with the value found for the $3+$ ions. Above the Curie temperature, they are all paramagnetic except Y, La, Yb and Lu. Ferromagnetism is found in the following metals: Eu, Gd, Tb, Dy, Ho and Er.[32,33,34,35,36] Gadolinium is the only metal to be ferromagnetic at room temperature and the Curie points decrease from 284°K (Gd) to 21°K (Er). An antiferromagnetic Néel point is observed with the following metals: Ce, Nd, Sm, Tb, Dy, Ho, Er, Tm.*

Specific heats. Specific heats have been measured over a wide temperature range, in many cases from 4°K to the melting point. Anomalies in the heat capacity–temperature plots are associated with transformations in the structure of the metal, or changes in its magnetic properties. Large magnetic anomalies are found in the ferromagnetic metals; these are particularly striking in the region of the Curie point.

Mechanical properties. The most important properties that have been studied are the Young modulus, shear modulus, Poisson's ratio and compressibility. The specific stiffness (E/ρ) of the rare earth metals compares unfavourably with that of other pure metals and alloys. This fact, together with their poor corrosion resistance, would seem to restrict any structural applications of the metals.

Yttrium metal has been produced on a relatively large scale, and much technological work has been carried out on metal

---

* Like paramagnetic substances, ferromagnetic substances are more permeable to a magnetic field than a vacuum. However, they show a marked field dependence, and approach a saturation magnetization as the field strength is increased. This is caused by a parallel alignment of magnetic moments. The temperature at which a paramagnetic material becomes ferromagnetic is called the Curie point.

Antiferromagnetic substances have lower susceptibilities than have paramagnetic substances, but they show a field dependence. This is caused by an antiparallel alignment of magnetic moments. The paramagnetic–antiferromagnetic transition temperature is called the Néel point.

References p. 141

fabrication techniques. Methods have been worked out for extrusion, swaging and reduction, and methods for machining the metal have been devised.[37]

Corrosion. A wide range of chemical reactivity is shown by the rare earth metals. The heavy earths, from gadolinium, together with samarium and yttrium, are inert at room temperature; a bright metal surface is retained after several weeks' exposure. But the light earth metals oxidise rapidly, the most reactive among them being lanthanum, cerium and europium. Oxide or hydroxide films form rapidly, their formation being probably catalysed by water vapour. Cerium and its alloy with iron (mischmetall) are both pyrophoric when finely divided.

At higher temperatures, the solid metals react with oxygen, hydrogen, nitrogen, or water vapour, and the molten metals are sufficiently reactive to attack many of the common refractory materials.

Chemical reactivity. The metals are rapidly attacked when immersed in water, the surface becoming dull and being rapidly pitted. They are attacked by all acids even at room temperature with one exception. A 50 : 50 mixture of concentrated nitric and hydrofluoric acids does not attack the heavy earth metals and yttrium at an appreciable rate.

CONCLUSIONS

All of the rare earth metals have now been prepared with purities greater than 99%. This is undoubtedly a remarkable technical achievement, particularly when compared with the situation ten years ago. However, the fact remains that many common metals can be prepared with considerably greater purity. This should be borne in mind when considering the present knowledge of the physical properties of the rare earth metals; some of these properties are very sensitive to the presence of trace impurities.

REFERENCES

1 HILLEBRAND and NORTON, *Pogg. Annal.*, 155 (1875) 631.
2 H. C. KRAMERS and R. G. STEVENS, *J. Am. Chem. Soc.*, 45 (1923) 614.
3 H. C. KRAMERS and H. BENKER, *Trans. Electrochem. Soc.*, 47 (1925) 353.
4 M. BILLY and F. TROMBE, *Compt. Rend.*, 193 (1931) 421.
5 F. TROMBE, *Compt. Rend.*, 194 (1932) 1653; 196 (1933) 704.
6 F. TROMBE, *Compt. Rend.*, 200 (1935) 459.
7 P. M. J. GRAY, *Trans. Inst. Mining Met.*, 61 (1951) 141.
8 W. MUNTHMANN, *Liebigs Annal.*, 320 (1902) 231.
9 B. PORTER, E. S. SHEDD, C. WYCHE, J. MARCHAND and R. G. KNICKER-
   BOCKER, *J. Metals*, 12 (1960) 798.
10 E. MORRICE, C. WYCHE and T. A. HENRIE, *U. S. Bur. Mines Rept. Invest.*,
   (1962) 6075.
11 W. KLEMM and H. BOMMER, *Z. Anorg. Allgem. Chem.*, 231 (1937) 138;
   241 (1939) 264.
12 H. BOMMER and E. HOHMANN, *Z. Anorg. Allgem. Chem.*, 241 (1939) 268.
13 F. TROMBE and F. MAHER, *Ann. Chem.*, 19 (1944) 345.
14 F. H. SPEDDING and A. H. DAANE, *J. Am. Chem. Soc.*, 74 (1952) 2783.
15 A. H. DAANE and F. H. SPEDDING, *J. Electrochem. Soc.*, 100 (1953) 442.
16 A. H. DAANE, D. H. DENNISON and F. H. SPEDDING, *J. Am. Chem. Soc.*,
   75 (1953) 2272.
17 F. H. SPEDDING, J. J. HANAK and A. H. DAANE, *Trans. A.I.M.E.*, 212
   (1958) 378.
18 C. E. HABERMANN and A. H. DAANE, *J. Less-Common Metals*, 5 (1963)
   134.
19 J. M. WILLIAMS and C. L. HOFFINE, *Nucl. Sci. Eng.*, 9 (1961) 500.
20 J. D. MARCHANT, E. S. SHEDD and T. A. HENRIE, *Rare Earth Research*,
   p. 143, Gordon & Breach, New York, 1962.
21 O. CARLSON, J. HAEFLING, F. SCHMIDT and F. H. SPEDDING, *J. Electrochem. Soc.*, 107 (1960) 540.
22 P. M. HALL, S. LEVGOLD and F. H. SPEDDING, *Phys. Rev.*, 116 (1959)
   1446.
23 H. E. NIGH, *J. Appl. Phys.*, 34 (1963) 3323.
24 C. W. KOCH, A. BROIDO and B. B. CUNNINGHAM, *J. Am. Chem. Soc.*,
   74 (1952) 2349.
25 C. W. KOCH and B. B. CUNNINGHAM, *J. Am. Chem. Soc.*, 75 (1953) 796
26 F. H. SPEDDING and A. H. DAANE, *Met. Rev.*, 5 (1960) 297.
27 P. W. BRIDGMAN, *Proc. Am. Acad. Arts Sci.*, 83 (1954) 1.
28 F. H. SPEDDING, J. J. HANAK and A. H. DAANE, *J. Less-Common Metals*.
   3 (1961) 110.
29 F. H. SPEDDING, A. H. DAANE and K. W. HERRMANN, *Acta Cryst.*, 9
   (1956) 559.
30 K. MENDELSSOHN and J. G. DAUNT, *Nature*, 139 (1937) 473.
31 D. H. PARKINSON, F. S. SIMON and F. H. SPEDDING, *Proc. Royal. Soc.*,
   207A (1951) 137.
32 G. URBAIN, P. WEISS and F. TROMBE, *Compt. Rend.*, 200 (1935) 2132.
33 F. TROMBE, *J. Rech. Centre Natl. Rech. Sci. Lab. Bellevue*, 23 (1953) 61.

34 J. F. ELLIOTT, S. LEVGOLD and F. H. SPEDDING, *Phys. Rev.*, 100 (1955) 1595.
35 C. H. LA BLANCHETAIS and F. TROMBE, *Compt. Rend.*, 243 (1956) 707.
36 W. C. THOBURN, S. LEVGOLD and F. H. SPEDDING, *Phys. Rev.*, 112 (1958) 56.
37 A. L. GEARY, A. GINDOBONI and P. LOWENSTEIN, *Rare Earth Research*, p. 105, Gordon & Breach, New York, 1962.
38 E. J. HUBER and C. E. HOLLEY, *J. Phys. Chem.*, 61 (1957) 497.
39 E. J. HUBER and C. E. HOLLEY, *J. Am. Chem. Soc.*, 75 (1953) 3594; 5645.
40 L. EYRING, H. R. LOHR and B. B. CUNNINGHAM, *J. Am. Chem. Soc.*, 74 (1952) 1186.
41 E. J. HUBER and C. E. HOLLEY, *J. Am. Chem. Soc.*, 74 (1952) 5530.
42 E. J. HUBER, C. O. MATTHEWS and C. E. HOLLEY, *J. Am. Chem. Soc.*, 77 (1958) 6493.
34 E. J. HUBER and C.E. HOLLEY, *J. Am. Chem. Soc.*, 77 (1955) 1444.
44 C. T. STUBBLEFIELD, H. EICK and L. EYRING, *J. Am. Chem. Soc.*, 78 (1956) 3877.
45 E. J. HUBER, E. L. HEAD and C. E. HOLLEY, *J. Phys. Chem.*, 60 (1956) 1457; 1582.
46 E. J. HUBER, E. L. HEAD and C. E. HOLLEY, *J. Phys. Chem.*, 61 (1957) 1021.
47 E. J. HUBER, E. L. HEAD and C. E. HOLLEY, *J. Phys. Chem.*, 64 (1960) 379; 1768.

CHAPTER 12

Applications of the rare earth elements

In considering the industrial application of the rare earth elements, it is necessary to remember two things. First, that the only two rare earth minerals at present being processed on a large scale are monazite and bastnaesite. In both minerals, 90 % of the rare earth portion consists of light earth elements. The early interest in monazite was due to the development of the incandescent gas mantle, and the discovery of the pyrophoric alloy mischmetall by AUER VON WELSBACH. Together these applications utilised both the thorium and the rare earth components of the mineral. These applications still retain importance in spite of electric bulbs having largely replaced gas lighting. The classical methods used for separating rare earths have been improved since these early developments, and this in turn has led to further applications of these materials, mainly in the optical industry. In the second place, one must remember that modern ion-exchange techniques capable of producing any of the rare earth elements in a state of high purity have been devised only in the last decade. Although many interesting outlets and potential applications of the heavy earth elements have been discovered during this period, it is questionable whether the processing of minerals such as xenotime solely for isolating and purifying heavy earth elements on a manufacturing scale is yet an economic proposition.

Applications of the rare earth elements fall readily into two classes. In the first category are well established uses, and in the second are a large number of possible applications that have emerged from recent research. It is too early to judge whether those in the second category will be eventually exploited and, if so, on what scale.

References p. 152

ESTABLISHED APPLICATIONS

Mischmetall. Much of the residual rare earth material from the extraction of thorium from monazite is used for manufacturing the pyrophoric 'mischmetall', an alloy of a number of rare earth metals.

It has been estimated that 25% of the rare earth materials available are utilised for this purpose in U.S.A.[1] The raw material, "technical cerium chloride", has the composition expressed as oxides: CeO_2 50%, La_2O_3 20–25%, Nd_2O_3 15–20%, other rare earths 10–15%. Metal is obtained by electrolysing the fused "technical cerium chloride", either alone or in presence of alkali or alkaline earth chlorides.

In the Austrian and German processes, electrolysis is carried out at 900° in refractory-lined steel cells, with carbon anodes and water-cooled steel cathodes. A potential of 12–14 V is applied, each cell requires a current of 2300 A, and the current efficiency varies from 40% to 45%. The cells are operated continuously for periods of from 2 to 3 weeks, and then require relining and charging with fresh electrolyte.[2, 3] The mischmetall produced contains some iron and silicon impurities. The pyrophoric properties of mischmetall are exploited in the production of special alloys for gas and cigarette lighter flints. These are made by alloying mischmetall with 30% of iron, which renders the product resistant to oxidation by air; small additions of magnesium (2%) and copper (1%) are also made to improve the properties of the alloy.

Technical grades of lanthanum, cerium, and neodymium metals can be manufactured by a process similar to that used for mischmetall; the appropriate chlorides are added to the electrolysis bath.

Uses in iron and steel manufacture. As normally manufactured, cast iron contains flakes of graphite which form points of stress concentration, the presence of which is a source of brittleness. However, the addition of small quantities of mischmetall to the melt, followed by a suitable heat treatment, causes the graphite to seperate in a nodular form.[4, 5] As the nodules do not form points of stress concentration, the mechanical properties of the product are markedly improved. This has made it feasible to cast engineering components that are to be subjected to high stresses.

A similar improvement to cast iron is, however, obtained by the addition of either magnesium or a magnesium alloy to the melt, and most of the 'nodular' cast iron has probably been produced by the addition of a magnesium–nickel alloy.[6] However, when the melt contains certain 'subversive' elements, such as Ti, Pb, Sn, Bi or Te, 'nodular' cast iron is not obtained by the simple addition of magnesium. For such irons the improvement is secured by the combined additions of magnesium and mischmetall.[7,8,9]

The quantity of mischmetall or cerium metal required to produce this result is small; it depends on the composition of the iron being treated, but rarely exceeds 1%. As, however, the production of nodular iron is now considerable, a good deal of rare earth material is required. Recent work has demonstrated that small additions of yttrium metal have the same effect as those of either cerium or magnesium.[10] The use of yttrium may have some advantage over the earlier processes, since the melting points of iron and yttrium are about the same. The function of the rare earth metal in producing nodular cast iron is not known, but its effect is probably due to the high affinity of the elements for such impurities as oxygen and sulphur.

Claims have been made that the addition of mischmetall (1–2%) to alloy and stainless steels improves the workability and yield of an ingot. The addition is made after the final de-oxidation of the steel, and processing is carried out in equipment lined with basic refractories.[11,12]

Miscellaneous metallurgical applications. Alloys of magnesium with rare earth metals are of industrial importance, since some of them have better mechanical properties and resistance to creep at temperatures up to 300° than any known magnesium alloy. The cerium–magnesium alloys carry from 0.5 to 6% of cerium metal, and the addition of a little of a second metal (Zr, Zn, or Mn) is beneficial.[13] The means by which creep resistance is conferred on the alloys has been discussed by RAYNOR.[14] Another potential application of the rare earth metals is in the processing of high melting metals. The mechanical properties of a number of these metals, for example Ta, Mo, V, and Cr, are very sensitive to the presence of even small quantities of impurities. An effective method of removing such impurities from vanadium is to arc-melt it with yttrium metal. The molten metals are virtually immiscible with one another, and the vanadium thus purified is ductile and may be cold-rolled.[15] Similarly, the solubility of the rare earth metals in molten chromium is small. Chromium alloyed with small quantities of rare earth metals, or particularly with yttrium, shows considerably improved resistance both to oxidation and nitride formation at elevated temperatures.[16,17] The action of the rare-earth metal in these applications is not completely understood, but its most important function is probably to act as a scavanger for trace impurities.

Optical and ceramic applications. Special preparations of ceric oxide are used on a large scale for polishing glass, particularly in the manufacture of ophthalmic and precision lenses. A range of technical ceric oxides is manufactured for this purpose, and it is claimed that their efficiency in polishing varies directly with the ceric oxide content.

The ceric ion absorbs very strongly in the ultra-violet range, and this property is exploited in the manufacture of special ophthalmic lenses (Crookes' glass) for use in bright sunlight. This glass usually contains from 2 % to 4 % of CeO_2. A more recent development, on similar lines, is the manufacture of ultra-violet absorbent glass containers for food affected by light; smaller quantities of CeO_2 are used for this purpose. But arsenic compounds must not be present, or yellow-brown colours are produced on exposure to sunlight.

To avoid a green colour in glasses it is necessary to oxidise the ferrous iron present to the ferric state. This is normally carried out chemically; and, if necessary, the yellow colour produced by the ferric ion is dealt with by the addition of a complementary colour. In certain special instances, the iron can be oxidised with ceric oxide.

High purity lanthanum oxide (> 99.95%) is used in the manufacture of glasses which have low dispersion and high refractive indexes. These glasses are essentially lanthanum borates, modified by small additions of barium silicate and zirconia, and have refractive indexes in the range n_D 1.69–1.70.[18] This type of glass is used in the manufacture of precision lens components.

Glasses manufactured from highly purified neodymium and praseodymium find application as special filters for calibrating optical instruments. This exploits the narrow absorption bands which are characteristic of the terpositive lanthanide ions (p. 117).

Glasses manufactured from 'didymium oxide', the technical mixture of neodymium and praseodymium oxides, have been used for many years in protective goggles in welding and other melting work. Recently, technically pure grades of neodymium and praseodymium oxides have become available, and glasses based on these oxides are being introduced into the field of decorative glassware. When added singly to a soda glass, violets and greens are obtained, and a wide variety of other colour effects are produced by other elements such as nickel or uranium. Neodymium, praseodymium, and erbium oxides have also been examined as constituents of ceramic glazes to be used in the manufacture of decorated pottery and coloured tiles. The metal cerates also have a limited application as ceramic glazes; for example the titanium compound is yellow.

Although electric lighting has largely displaced gas lighting in industrial areas, gas mantles are still manufactured on a large scale. Woven rayon formers are impregnated with a concentrated solution of a pure grade of thorium nitrate, to which small quantities of cerium nitrate, aluminium nitrate, or alkaline earth nitrates are added. After drying, the formers are marked with a "didymium" nitrate solution, and the metal hydroxides are precipitated by immersing the formers in ammonia. The formers are moulded to shape and dried; finally the fibrous support is burnt off and the remaining oxides are ignited strongly. The finished mantle consists essentially of a thoria ceramic, containing a small quantity (approx. 1 %) of ceria, which confers the incandescent property.

An allied use of the rare earth elements is to form incandescent cores for carbons used in arc lighting. The fluorides of technical grade light earths are used for this purpose.

POTENTIAL APPLICATIONS OF THE RARE EARTH ELEMENTS

Ceramics. The rare-earth oxides have high melting points, and are very stable chemically. Nevertheless, attempts to prepare ceramic bodies from the light earth oxides have met with little success, and products from these oxides rehydrate after firing. ROY has attributed this to the difference in structure of the light and heavy earth oxides, and suggests that the unsymmetrical A structure is more readily hydrated than the C form[19] (p. 85). More success has been obtained with yttria and the heavy earth oxides, which have the C structure. The addition of yttria is effective in preventing the phase change of zirconia ceramic ware; the tetragonal form is stabilised by the addition of 6 % of Y_2O_3.[20]

The rare earth sulphides are also very refractory, and appear to be free from some of the disadvantages of the corresponding oxides, although they can be used only in an inert atmosphere. The cerium sulphides have received attention as special-purpose high temperature refractories.[21,22] The monosulphide, CeS, melts at 2450°, and has a vapour pressure of 10^{-3} mm at 1900°. It was possible to make crucibles of this material with less than 1 % porosity that were resistant to thermal shock, and these were not attacked by molten Ce, U, Mg, Fe, or Zn metals. Platinum did however react to give $CePt_2$. The sulphide Ce_3S_4 is also refractory, but is not as resistant to thermal shock as CeS, and, moreover, forms a eutectic with the oxosulphide Ce_2O_2S which melts at 1750°.

Semiconducting and other electrical properties. A number of investigations have been made of the semiconducting and thermoelectric properties of rare earth compounds. The main attention has been given to selenides and tellurides, although some work has been reported on the bismuthides and antimonides.

The preparation of selected rare earth selenides, tellurides, bismuthides and antimonides has been described, and electrical and other measurements have been made on representative selenides and tellurides of well-defined composition.[23] With those of Ce, Nd and Gd, resistivities and Seebeck coefficients measured at room temperature showed a maximum just below the Ln_2X_3 composition (p. 107). Both samarium and yttrium compounds had a maximum resistivity at the LnX composition.[24] An examination of the Gd–Se system showed that the resistivity reached a peak value below the composition Gd_2Se_3 and that the resistivity of the Gd_2Se_3 compound decreased rapidly above 500°.[25] Other work indicated that the monoselenide had a low resistivity and Seebeck coefficient; however, a composition corresponding to $GdSe_{1.4}$, when quenched from 1800°, had a high resistivity and Seebeck coefficient.[26] The materials examined in the last two investigations were not well characterised, and their resistivity and Seebeck coefficient results showed substantial differences from those reported by other workers.

The thermoelectric properties of some simple and compound cerium sulphide compositions have been examined. Compositions within the range Ce_3S_4 to Ce_2S_3 had the thorium phosphide structure, and to some of the materials strontium sulphide was added in a controlled quantity to preserve the lattice structure.[27] The resistivity and Seebeck coefficients of the sulphides increased with temperature. The addition of strontium sulphide did not alter the sense of the temperature dependance of these two properties, but usually their actual values were less. The thermoelectric figure of merit for the compound $CeS_{1.37}$ $SrS_{0.38}$ increased with temperature from 0° to 1200°.*

Another potentially important application is in the field of

---

* The thermoelectric figure of merit is $\dfrac{\alpha^2}{\rho\kappa}$ where α is the Seebeck coefficient, ρ the resistivity, and κ the thermal conductivity.

electronic ceramics. The rare earth titanates and stannates have large dielectric constants and small temperature coefficients of capacitance, and may accordingly be used as capacitors.

The rare earth hexaborides have low work functions and high thermionic emission currents (p. 76). This combination of properties suggests that the materials would be useful filament materials in special purpose electronic valves.[28]

Masers and Lasers. Radio masers are electronic devices used for effecting amplification at a very low noise level. Among the early materials considered for this purpose were mixed crystals of the rare earth ethyl sulphates and of their antipyrene iodides, both of which can be grown as single crystals from aqueous solutions. More recently, the rare earth garnets, of composition $3 Ln_2O_3.5 Fe_2O_3$, have received extensive attention, in particular the yttrium compound. Single crystals of such garnets can be grown from melts, and the properties of a number of them have been examined.

Optical masers depend for their operation on similar physical principles to those applying to the radio maser, but they are stimulated by radiation in the light range and then emit light restricted to a very narrow wavelength. Certain of the rare earths have found application in this field, as some of their compounds emit light in the visible and near-visible regions when suitably excited. The absorption bands of the terpositive elements are narrow, and their fluorescent lines are sharp; those of the bipositive lanthanides are broad, but their fluorescent lines are sharp. In practice, rare earth ions, usually in low concentration, are introduced into a host lattice by growing single crystals of the mixture. Thus, the scheelite structure ($CaWO_4$) will accommodate all the terpositive Ln^{3+} ions but only Eu^{2+} of the bipositive ions. Fluorite, CaF_2, will accommodate bi- and terpositive lanthanide ions. Certain of the rare earth glasses, for example neodymium glass, may also be used. Similar effects have been obtained with an organic compound of europium.

Nuclear applications. In this area there are three applications of the rare earth elements. The first utilises the exceptional neutron absorption properties of some isotopes of rare earth elements. For reactor control rods, Eu, Dy or a Gd–Er mixture appear to have the right combination of properties. Suitable quantities of the oxides are incorporated into steel or cermet rods.[29]

The second application takes advantage of the gamma radiation emitted by thulium after neutron irradiation. This is a soft radiation, with a 127 d half-life. The source usually takes the form of a fired thulia pellet, encapsulated in aluminium. These are useful for the radiography of light, inaccessible structures such as the electrodes of radio valves and also find application for thickness gauging of thin steel or light alloy sheet. For general radiography, their employment is limited to cases where cheapness or mobility are important. Their use in medical radiography is also limited.

The third application exploits the ability of semiconductors to convert radioactive energy into electrical energy. A thin layer of radioactive material is sandwiched between alternative slices of p- and n-type semiconductor, usually silicon, and a miniature battery is formed by stacking a number of these layers together. The β-radiation from ^{147}Pm is very suitable for this purpose, and methods have been perfected for isolating high-purity fission-product promethium on a kilogram scale.[30] This type of battery has a life of over five years and can operate in extreme temperatures. Suggested applications are in miniature transmitters and receivers in meteorological stations, submarine cables, space probes and satellites.

Superconductivity. A material is said to have superconducting properties when its resistivity effectively becomes zero. This remarkable property is shown by a number of metals and alloys at very low temperatures. Lanthanum metal becomes superconducting at 5°K, and this property is also found in certain rare earth alloys.[31] A number of these are Laves compounds with the platinum metals, such as YPt_2, YRh_2, and YOs_2. An alloy of indium and lanthanum, of composition $InLa_3$, becomes superconducting at 10.4°K.

References p. 152

Certain rare earth compounds have the property of altering the polarisation of a light beam in a magnetic field. This property was exploited by BECQUEREL in the study of paramagnetic properties at low temperatures.[32] An interesting development of this has been the observation of domain effects in superconductors at low temperatures. Thin films of cerium salts, or cerium phosphate glasses, are applied to the surface of the superconductor and the domain effects are viewed in polarised light.[33, 34, 35]

Magnetic properties. Six of the rare earth metals are ferromagnetic. Their Curie temperatures (p. 139) are as follows: Eu, $-165°$; Gd, $17°$; Tb, $-36°$; Dy, $-188°$; Ho, $-253°$; and Er, $-254°$.[36-44] This property does not appear to have been exploited. Ferromagnetism has also been reported at very low temperatures in a number of europous compounds.[44, 45]

Magnetic cooling. The use of magnetic cooling to produce very low temperatures was introduced by KAMERLINGH ONNES in 1923. He reduced temperatures to below $1°K$ in this way,[47] and used gadolinium sulphate for this purpose, the salt being enclosed in a vacuum system cooled externally with liquid helium. After cooling to about $1°K$, the gadolinium sulphate is magnetised in a powerful field and becomes warm. This energy is dissipated by boiling the helium under a low pressure. The salt falls to a lower temperature when the magnetic field is switched off. Other rare earth salts which show this effect and have been used for this purpose include cerium fluoride and the ethyl sulphates of cerium and dysprosium.[48]

REFERENCES

1 C. A. HAMPEL, *Glass Ind.*, 41 (1960) 15; 82; 148.
2 *The cerium industry in German territory*, B.I.O.S. Report No. 400.
3 *The cerium metal and lighter flint industry in Germany and Austria*, F.I.A.T. Report No. 909, September 1946.
4 British Patent 645,862 to B.C.I.R.A.
5 British Patent 649,946 to B.C.I.R.A.
6 British Patent 630,070 to International Nickel Company.

7 British Patent 685,083 to International Nickel Company.

8 British Patent 723,992 to International Nickel Company.

9 British Patent 718,177 to B.C.I.R.A.

10 J. J. KANTER, J. P. MAGOS and W. L. MEINHART, *Foundry*, 90 (1962) 52.

11 G. CHEETHAM, *Iron Coal Rev.*, 171 (1955) 15.

12 W. J. JACKSON, *Metallurgia*, 54 (1956) 233.

13 G. A. MELLOR and R. W. RIDLEY, *J. Inst. Metals*, 75 (1948-9) 679; 81 (1952-3) 245.

14 G. V. RAYNOR, *The Physical Metallurgy of Magnesium and its Alloys*, *Chapter 11*, Pergamon Press, Oxford.

15 E. M. SAVITSKII and V. F. TEREKHOVA, *Tsvetnye Metally*, 32 (1959) 48.

16 E. M. SAVITSKII, V. V. BARON and Y. V. EFIMOV, *Akad. Nauk S.S.S.R. Met i Tophiv.*, 3 (1962) 107.

17 N. E. RYAN, *J. Less-Common Metals*, 6 (1964) 21.

18 U.S. Patent 2, 745,757 to W. G. GEFFCKEN, 15-5-1956.

19 M. W. SHAFER and R. ROY, *J. Am. Ceram. Soc.*, 42 (1959) 563.

20 P. DUWEZ. F. BROWN and F. ODELL, *J. Electrochem. Soc.*, 98 (1951) 356.

21 E. D. EASTMAN, L. BREWER, L. A. BROMLEY, P. W. GILLIS and N. L. LOFGREN, *J. Am. Chem. Soc.*, 72 (1950) 2248.

22 E. D. EASTMAN, L. BREWER *et al.*, *J. Am. Ceram. Soc.*, 34 (1951) 128.

23 J. F. MILLER and R. C. HIMES, Rare Earths Research Conference, 1960.

24 J. F. MILLER, L. K. MATSON and R. C. HIMES, Rare Earths Research Conference, 1962.

25 R. C. VICKERY and H. M. MUIR, Rare Earths Research Conference, 1960.

26 R. C. VICKERY and H. M. MUIR, *Nature*, 190 (1961) 336.

27 F. M. RYAN, I. N. GREENBERG, F. L. CARTER and R. C. MILLER, *J. Appl. Phys.*, 33 (1962) 846.

28 G. SAMSANOV, *Usp. Khim.*, 28 (1959) 189.

29 J. A. RANSOHOFF, *Nucleonics*, 17 (7) (1959) 80.

30 E. J. WHEELWRIGHT and F. P. ROBERTS, U.S.A.E.C. Report HW 78651, 1963.

31 K. MENDELSSOHN and J. G. DAUNT, *Nature*, 139 (1937) 437.

32 J. BECQUEREL and W. J. DE HAAS, *Comm. Univ. Leiden, Suppl.*, 74 (1933) 20.

33 P. B. ALERS, *Phys. Rev.*, 105 (1957) 104.

34 P. B. ALERS, *Phys. Rev.*, 116 (1959) 1482.

35 W. DESORBO, *Phys. Rev. Letters*, 4 (1960) 406.

36 C. H. LA BLANCHETAIS and F. TROMBE, *Compt. Rend.*, 243 (1956) 707.

37 G. URBAIN, P. WEISS and F. TROMBE, *Compt. Rend.*, 200 (1935) 2132.

38 J. F. ELLIOTT, S. LEVGOLD and F. H. SPEDDING, *Phys. Rev.*, 91 (1953) 28.

39 F. TROMBE, *Compt. Rend.*, 221 (1945) 19.

40 F. TROMBE, *Compt. Rend.*, 236 (1953) 591.

41 D. R. BEHRENDT, S. LEVGOLD and F. H. SPEDDING, *Phys. Rev.*, 109 (1958) 1544.

42 W. C. THOBURN, S. LEVGOLD and F. H. SPEDDING, *Phys. Rev.*, 122 (1958) 56.

43 B. L. RHODES, S. LEVGOLD and F. H. SPEDDING, *Phys. Rev.*, 109 (1958) 1547.

44 J. F. ELLIOTT, S. LEVGOLD and F. H. SPEDDING, *Phys. Rev.*, 100 (1955) 1595.
45 T. R. McGUIRE, B. ARGYLE, M. W. SHAFER and J. SMART, *J. Appl. Phys.*, 34 (1963) 1345.
46 M. W. SHAFER, T. R. McGUIRE and J. SUITS, *Phys. Rev. Letters*, 11 (1963) 251.
47 H. R. WOLTJER and H. KAMERLINGH ONNES, *Proc. Acad. Sci. Amsterdam*, 32 (1923) 772.
48 E. AMBLER and R. P. HUDSON, *Rep. Progr. Phys.*, 18 (1955) 251.

Pages 156–159 incl.:

ISOTOPES OF RARE EARTH ELEMENTS
PRODUCED BY PILE RADIATION

ISOTOPES OF RARE EARTH ELEMENTS

Element	Atomic Number	Stable isotopes, Abundance%		Activation cross-section (Barns)	Target material	Isotope produced
Y	39	^{89}Y	100	1.3	Y_2O_3	^{90}Y
La	57	^{139}La	99.9	8.2	La_2O_3	^{140}La
Ce	58	^{136}Ce	0.19			^{139}Ce
		^{138}Ce	0.25			
		^{140}Ce	88.5	0.27	CeO_2	^{141}Ce
		^{142}Ce	11.1	0.10		^{143}Ce
				0.10		^{143}Pr
Pr	59	^{141}Pr	100	11	Pr_6O_{11}	^{142}Pr
						^{143}Pr
Nd	60	^{146}Nd	17.2	0.31	Nd_2O_3	^{147}Nd
		^{148}Nd	5.7	0.21		^{149}Nd
		^{150}Nd	5.6	0.084		^{151}Nd
				0.31		^{147}Pm
				0.21		^{149}Pm
						^{151}Pm
Pm	61	No stable isotopes			See Nd	
Sm	62	^{150}Sm	7.4	–		^{151}Sm
		^{152}Sm	26.6	37	Sm_2O_3	^{153}Sm
		^{154}Sm	22.5	1.25		^{155}Sm
				1.25		^{155}Eu
Eu	63	^{151}Eu	47.8	670	Eu_2O_3	^{152m}Eu
				3360		^{152}Eu
		^{153}Eu	52.2	220		^{154}Eu
				1.25	$^{154}Sm_2O_3$	^{155}Eu
Gd	64	^{152}Gd	0.2	0.25	Gd_2O_3	^{153}Gd
		^{158}Gd	24.6	1.0		^{159}Gd
		^{160}Gd	21.7	0.175		^{161}Gd
				0.175		^{161}Tb
Tb	65	^{159}Tb	100	22	Tb_4O_7	^{160}Tb
						^{161}Tb
Dy	66	^{164}Dy	28.2	790	Dy_2O_3	^{165}Dy
Ho	67	^{165}Ho	100	60	Ho_2O_3	^{166}Ho

PRODUCED BY PILE RADIATION

Half life	Specific activity produced †	β (MeV)	γ (MeV)	Decay
64.2 h	190 mC	2.25	None	$^{90}Y \rightarrow ^{90}Zr$ st.
40.2 h	860 mC	$2.20 - \langle 0.83$	$2.54 - 0.33$	$^{140}La \rightarrow ^{140}Ce$ st.
140 d	—	KEC	0.166	$^{139}Ce \rightarrow ^{139}La$ st.
32.5 d	3.7 mC	0.58, 0.44	0.145	$^{141}Ce \rightarrow ^{141}Pr$ st.
33 h	11 mC	$1.40 - 0.30$	$1.10 - 0.057$	$^{143}Ce \rightarrow ^{143}Pr$
13.8 d	*	0.93	None	$^{143}Pr \rightarrow ^{143}Nd$ st.
19.2 h See cerium	1.3 C	2.15, 0.58	1,57	$^{142}Pr \rightarrow ^{142}Nd$ st.
11.1 d	11 mC	$0.81 - 0.21$	$0.69 - 0.09$	$^{147}Nd \rightarrow ^{147}Pm$
1.8 h	24 mC	$1.5 - 0.95$	$0.65 - 0.03$	$^{149}Nd \rightarrow ^{149}Pm$
12 m	9.4 mC	$2.06 - 1.2$	$0.43 - 0.117$	$^{151}Nd \rightarrow ^{151}Pm$
2.6 y	*	0.22	None	$^{147}Pm \rightarrow ^{147}Sm$ st.
53 h	*	1.07, 0.78	0.285	$^{149}Pm \rightarrow ^{149}Sm$ st.
28 h	4.2 mC	1.1	$0.715 - 0.065$	$^{151}Pm \rightarrow ^{151}Sm$
93 y		0.075	0.02	$^{151}Sm \rightarrow ^{151}Eu$ st.
47 h	3.5 C	$0.80 - 0.63$	$0.61 - 0.07$	$^{153}Sm \rightarrow ^{153}Eu$ st.
22 m	130 mC	1.65, 1.50	$0.246 - 0.104$	$^{155}Sm \rightarrow ^{155}Eu$
1.7 y	*	$0.25 - 0.15$	0.105, 0.087	$^{155}Eu \rightarrow ^{155}Gd$ st.
9.3 h	70 C	$1.87 - 0.56$, EC	$1.39 - 0.12$	$^{152}Eu \rightarrow ^{152}Gd$ st. $^{152m}Eu \rightarrow ^{152}Sm$ st.
13 y	310 mC	$1.47 - 0.22$, EC	$1.41 - 0.12$	$^{152}Eu \rightarrow ^{152}Gd$
16 y	17 mC	$1.84 - 0.15$	$1.28 - 0.12$	$^{154}Eu \rightarrow ^{154}Gd$
1.7 y	see Sm			
236 d	450 μC	EC	$0.103 - 0.07$	$^{153}Gd \rightarrow ^{153}Eu$ st.
18.0 h	63 mC	$0.94 - 0.58$	0.36	$^{159}Gd \rightarrow ^{159}Tb$ st.
3.6 m	18 mC	1.5	$0.52 - 0.05$	$^{161}Gd \rightarrow ^{161}Tb$
7.0 d	*	$0.61 - 0.4$	$0.07 - 0.03$	$^{161}Tb \rightarrow ^{161}Dy$ st.
73 d See Gd	120 mC	$1.71 - 0.3$	$1.27 - 0.09$	$^{160}Tb \rightarrow ^{160}Dy$ st.
2.3 h	80 C	$1.31 - 0.31$	$0.71 - 0.09$	$^{165}Dy \rightarrow ^{165}Ho$ st.
27 h	5.7 C	$1.84 - 0.23$	$1.69 - 0.08$	$^{166}Ho \rightarrow ^{166}Er$ st.

(continued)

Element	Atomic Number	Stable isotopes, Abundance %		Activation cross-section (Barns)	Target material	Isotope produced
Er	68	^{168}Er	27.07	0.54	Er_2O_3	^{169}Er
		^{170}Er	14.88	1.3		^{171}Er
						^{171}Tm
Tm	69	^{169}Tm	100	130	Tm_2O_3	^{170}Tm
Yb	70	^{168}Yb	0.14	15.4	Yb_2O_3	^{169}Yb
		^{174}Yb	31.8	19		^{175}Yb
		^{176}Yb	12.6	0.70		^{177}Yb
						^{177}Lu
Lu	71	^{175}Lu	97.4	34	Lu_2O_3	^{176m}Lu
		^{176}Lu	2.6			^{176}Lu
				100		^{177}Lu
						^{177}Lu

† Specify activity produced per gram of target element by thermal flux of 10^{12} n/cm²sec for one week.

* Specific activity produced depends upon time elapsed after irradiation.

Half life	Specific activity produced†	β (MeV)	y (MeV)	Decay
9.4 d	19 mC	0.34	none	^{169}Er $\rightarrow$ ^{169}Tm st.
7.5 h	87 mC	1.5 – 0.55	0.31 – 0.11	^{171}Er $\rightarrow$ ^{171}Tm
1.9 y	*	0.1, 0.03	0.06	^{171}Tm $\rightarrow$ ^{171}Yb st.
127 d	390 mC	0.97, 0.88	0.084	^{170}Tm $\rightarrow$ ^{170}Yb st.
31 d	180 mC	EC 100%	0.31 – 0.008	^{169}Yb $\rightarrow$ ^{169}Tm st.
4.2 d	1.1 C	0.47 – 0.07	0.396 – 0.114	^{175}Yb $\rightarrow$ ^{175}Lu st.
1.9 h	66 mC	1.38 – 0.16	1.24 – 0.12	^{177}Yb $\rightarrow$ ^{177}Lu
6.75 d	*	0.5 – 0.17	0.32 – 0.07	^{177}Lu $\rightarrow$ ^{177}Hf st.
3.7 h	3.2 C	1.2, 1.1	0.089	^{176m}Lu $\rightarrow$ ^{176}Hf st.
2.4 × 10^{10} y	Naturally active	0.4	0.31 – 0.09	^{176}Lu $\rightarrow$ ^{176}Hf st.
6.75 d	4.3 C	0.50 – 0.17	0.32 – 0.07	
see also ytterbium				

1. R. A. ALLEN, D. B. SMITH and J. E. HISCOTT, *Radioisotope Data*, A.E.R.E.-Report 2938, 1961.

Subject Index

Absorption spectra of lanthanides, 117

Abundance of rare-earth elements, 6, 17

Acetates, 47

Acetylacetonates, 50

Actinide elements, 7, 10, 12

Activity coefficients of lanthanide chlorides, 55

Alkoxides, 50

Alloys of lanthanides with magnesium, 145

Aluminium sulphide, 98, 102

Amalgam extraction, 26, 37, 39

Analytical determination of rare earths, 114 *et seq.*

Antimonides, 81

Apatite, 14, 23

Applications of rare-earth elements, 143 *et seq.*

Arc melting of lanthanide metals, 131

Arsenides, 81

Atomic-beam resonance with rare-earth elements, 7

Atomic volume of rare-earth ions, 11

Atomic weight of rare-earth elements, 2

Basicity separation of rare-earth elements, 23

Bastnaesite, 15, 19, 21, 23, 143

Bipositive lanthanides, 49

Bismuthides, 82

Borates, 45

Borides, 74 *et seq.*
   potential applications of, 150

Bromides, 42, 53, 64, 66, 133

Carbides, 76 *et seq.*

Carbonates, 44, 65

Carbonate double salts, 47

Cast iron, effect of addition of lanthanides on, 144

Ceramic application of lanthanides, 146, 148

Ceric–cerous couple, 59, 115

Ceric halides, 48
   hydroxide, 48
   iodate, 48
   nitrate, 48
   sulphate, 48
   oxide, 85, 92, 114, 115

Ceric-salt solutions, nature of, 56

Cerous compounds, oxidation of, 27, 49

Chalcogenides, 66
   structure of, 111

Charge number of rare-earth elements, 8, 10, 11, 14, 27

Chlorides, 42, 63, 64, 66, 99, 100, 107, 109, 133

Chromates, 45

Citric acid as complexing agent, 28

Complex-ion formation, 57

Conductivity of aqueous lanthanide salt solutions, 53

Crookes' glass, 146

Cupric ions, use in ion-exchange chromatographic separations of lanthanides, 33

Curie temperature, 139, 152

Cyanides, 46

Cyclopentadienides, 50

DCTA (1:2-diaminocyclohexanetetraacetic acid), 58
Deuterides, 71
Dialkyl phosphoric acids, 35
Di (2-ethylhexyl) phosphoric acid, 36
Dimethyl phosphates, 47
Dioctyl phosphoric acid, 36
Displacement-development chromatography, 29
Distribution factor, 30
Double ammonium nitrates, 5
DTPA (diethylenetriaminepentaacetic acid), 58

EDTA (ethylenediaminetetraacetic acid), 30, 38, 58, 116
EEDTA (2:2-bis{2-di(carboxymethyl)amino}ethyl ether), 58
EGTA (1:2-bis{2-di(carboxymethyl) aminoethoxy}ethane), 58
Ekaboron, 4
Electronic ceramics, 150
Electronic configuration of rare-earth elements, 6, 8, 10
Emission spectra of lanthanides, 119
Entropy changes on complex formation, 57
Epidote, 15
Ethyl sulphates, 47
Europous compounds, 27, 28, 65
Euxenite, 14, 16, 19, 20
Extraction of lanthanides from minerals, 19 et seq.

f electrons in rare-earth elements, 8
Fermi level, 76
Fluoride, 42, 43, 64, 67, 68, 133, 148
    double salts, 67
    reduction of, 128
Fluorite, 15, 150
Fluorocarbonates, 24
Formates, 47
Frontal analysis, 28, 29

Gadolinite, 2, 14, 15
Gallium sulphide, 102
Garnets, rare-earth bearing, 150

Gas mantles, 143, 147
Glasses containing rare earths, 147
Gravimetric estimation of
    cerium, 114
    lanthanides, 115
    mean equivalent weight, 116

Halides, 42, 48, 63, 64, 65, 66, 99, 100
    electrolysis of, 125 et seq., 144
Heavy earths, definition of term, 2
HEEDTA (β-hydroxyethylene diaminetetraacetic acid), 58
Helium, 21
Higher-valency states of lanthanides, 47, 67, 88
Hund rules, 10
Hydrides, 71 et seq., 99
Hydrolysis of lanthanide ions, 27, 56
Hydroxides, 23, 27, 44, 48, 65, 93
β-Hydroxyethylethylenediamine triacetic acid, 32

Iodates, 43, 48, 114
Iodides, 43, 64, 66, 133
Ion-exchange chromatography, 1, 26 28, 38, 121
Ion-exchange membranes, 37, 39
Ionic sizes of lanthanide ions, 12, 68
Ion-pair formation, 54
Isotopes of rare-earth elements, 2, 122, 156 et seq.

Jones-reductor reductions, 65, 115

Lanthanide contraction, 12
Lanthanum oxide, high purity, 147
Lanthanum ferrocyanide, 54
Laser materials, 150
Ligand exchange, 33
Light earths, definition of term, 2
Lower valency states, 63, 91

Magnetic measurements for assessment of charge state of rare-earth elements, 11, 66, 67
Magnetic moments of terpositive lanthanides, 10, 11

Maser materials containing lanthanides, 150
Mesothorium, 21
Metals, 98, 125 et seq.
    chemical reactivities of, 140
    crystallographic data for, 136, 137
    distillation of, 130
    magnetic properties of, 139, 152
    mechanical properties of, 139
    physical properties of, 133 et seq., 151, 152
    preparation of, 125 et seq.
    purification of, 132
    single crystals of, 132
    structure of, 73
    superconductivity of, 151
Metallothermic reduction of lanthanide compounds, 128
Middle earth, definition of term, 2
Minerals of rare-earth elements, 14 et seq.
Mischmetall, 143, 144, 145
Mixed-oxide systems, 93 et seq.
Molar absorptivities of rare-earth elements, 118
Molybdates, 45
Monazite, 14, 15, 17, 19, 20, 23, 143, 144

Nitrates, 34, 42, 46, 48, 53
    double salts, 46
Nitrides, 80 et seq.
Nitromethane as extractant for cerium, 36
Nuclear properties of lanthanides, 150, 156 et seq.

Oddo and Harkins rule, 18
Onsager equation, 54
Optical applications of rare-earth elements, 146
Organic salts, 47
Oxalates, 22, 24, 44, 115, 116, 117
    double salts, 46, 115, 116
Oxides, 85 et seq.
    electrolysis of, 74, 78, 127
    heat of formation, 138

non-stoicheiometric, 85, 87 et seq.
    structure, 85
    structure of rare-earth oxide–metal oxide compounds, 95
Oxohalides, 43
Oxoselenides, 108
Oxotellurides, 110

Paramagnetism, 9
Paramagnetic properties of lanthanides, 9
Partition coefficient, 35
Perchlorates, 55
Phosphates, 22, 24, 45
Phosphides, 81
Polarography of lanthanides, 119
Polycrase, 16
Position of rare earths in periodic system, 5
Potash feldspars, 15
Promethium, 1, 156
Pulsed columns for solvent extraction, 39

Reduction potentials of lanthanide ions, 59, 60

Samarous compounds, 64, 65
Scandium, 2, 18
Selenates, 44
Selenides, 106 et seq.
    applications of, 149
    useful physical properties of, 149
Separation,
    of rare earths, 26 et seq., 120 et seq.
    of cerium, 27
    of europium, 27
Separation factors, 34, 39
Silicates, 45
Silicides, 78 et seq.
Sodium amalgam, 37
Solvent extraction, use in separation of rare earths, 23, 26, 34 et seq., 38

Spectra of rare-earth elements, 7, 117 *et seq.*
Stannates, 95
Sulphates, 43, 48, 54, 65, 67, 101
   double salts, 22, 26, 27, 46, 116
Sulphate-separation processes for rare earths, 26, 38
Sulphides, 65, 98 *et seq.*
   applications of, 148
   double salts of, 101
   electrolysis of, 99
   melting points of, 105, 148
   structure of, 103
Sulphites, 43

Tellurides, 109, 110
   useful physical properties of, 149
Thermionic emission current, 76, 150
Thermoelectric properties, 90, 92, 149
Thiosulphates, 44
Thorium–rare-earth phosphate oxalate, 22

Thoron, 21
Thortveitite, 19
Transport numbers, 54
TRILO (nitrolotriacetic acid), 58

Valency states of lanthanides, 69
Volumetric estimation of
   cerium, 115
   europium, 115
   mean equivalent weight, 116
   total lanthanides, 116

Work function, 76

Xenotime, 14, 15, 18, 20, 21, 24, 143
X-ray fluorescent spectra of lanthanides, 120

Yttrium, 2, 13, 14, 16, 27, 136, 138

Zinc amalgam, 36
Zirconia, 94, 148